SRA Imagine It!

Skills Practice
Annotated Teacher's Edition

Level 5
Book 1

McGraw Hill · SRA

Columbus, OH

SRAonline.com

 SRA

Send all inquiries to this address:
SRA/McGraw-Hill
4400 Easton Commons
Columbus, OH 43219-6188

ISBN: 978-0-07-610496-3
MHID: 0-07-610496-6

2 3 4 5 6 7 8 9 QPD 13 12 11 10 09 08

The *McGraw·Hill* Companies

Table of Contents

Unit 1 Heritage

Unit 2 Energy at Work

Unit 3 Making a New Nation

Name _____ **Date** _____

Root Words

Focus Many words contain **root words** that come from languages other than English. For example, *bicycle* and *recycle* both contain the Greek root *cycl,* which means "circle." Knowing the meaning of a root can help you learn the meanings of words that use the same root. However, a word's literal meaning is often different from a word's common English meaning. *Cyclone* literally means "to go around in a circle." Its actual meaning is "a storm of winds that revolve around a center, such as a tornado."

Practice **Each word is followed by its root word and the root's definition. Choose two words from the box that use the same root word, and write them on the lines.**

thermal	enact	produce	thermostat
dislocate	locate	react	conduct

1. education; root word *duc,* meaning "to lead"

    produce   conduct

2. action; root word *act,* meaning "to do"

    react   enact

3. location; root word *loc,* meaning "place"

    locate   dislocate

4. thermometer; root word *therm,* meaning "heat"

    thermostat   thermal

 Each word below is followed by a literal definition. Use a dictionary to find its actual definition, and then use the word in a sentence.

5. allocate = to place

Possible Answer The manager allocated funds for a yearly company picnic.

6. activate = to drive or do

Possible Answer He tried to activate the device but was unsuccessful.

7. egocentric = oneself being the center

Possible Answer Jeremy is very egocentric and thus not a very good teammate.

8. aqueduct = to lead water

Possible Answer The tour guide told us the aqueduct was important to the process of supplying the city with its water.

Name _____ Date _____

Selection Vocabulary

Focus

propped (propd) *adj.* supported by something under or against (page 24)

edible (ed' • ə • bəl) *adj.* fit or safe to eat (page 27)

lingered (lin' • gərd) *v.* past tense of **linger:** to be slow in leaving (page 28)

inspired (in • spīrd') *v.* influenced (page 29)

unjustly (un • just' • lē) *adv.* unfairly (page 30)

persecuted (pûr' • si • kyūt' • əd) *v.* past tense of **persecute:** to treat in a cruel and unjust way (page 30)

logic (lo' • jik) *n.* a way of thinking about something (page 31)

apparently (ə • par' • ənt • lē) *adv.* as far as one can judge by the way things appear (page 33)

assumed (ə • sōōmd') *v.* past tense of **assume:** to take for granted (page 34)

reality (rē • al' • i • tē) *n.* something actual or real (page 34)

Practice Write the vocabulary word next to the group of words that have a similar meaning.

1. without cause; unfairly; unequally _____unjustly_____

2. thought; judgement; reason _____logic_____

3. encouraged; motivated; uplifted _____inspired_____

4. seemingly; evidently _____apparently_____

5. actuality; fact; existence _____reality_____

6. delayed; lagged _____lingered_____

7. tormented; mistreated; wronged _____persecuted_____

8. eatable; consumable ___edible___

9. supposed; presumed ___assumed___

10. supported; up against ___propped___

 **Apply** **Fill in each blank with a word from the word box that best completes each sentence.**

lingered	unjustly	reality	assumed	apparently
logic	propped	edible	persecuted	inspired

11. Mr. Sheer ___assumed___ we had studied for the test.

12. This is ___apparently___ the tallest hill in the city.

13. I ___propped___ up my sprained ankle on the chair.

14. The meat was left out all night and is no longer ___edible___.

15. We will have to use ___logic___ to solve this puzzle!

16. The crowd ___unjustly___ taunted the visiting team.

17. The ___reality___ is that we cannot afford a new car.

18. Kristy had the thought that her brother was ___persecuted___ by the bullies at school.

19. The speech ___inspired___ the entire class to stand up and clap.

20. Because she did not want to leave, she ___lingered___ by the door.

Name _____ Date _____

Author's Point of View

Focus

Writers must decide from whose point of view they will tell a story.

- **First-person point of view** is told through the eyes of a character in the story. First-person narrators use words such as *I, me, we, us, our,* and *my.*

- **Third-person point of view** is told through the eyes of a narrator who is outside the story. Third-person narrators use words such as *he, she, her, them, theirs, his,* and *hers.*

Practice

Read the following paragraph from "The Land I Lost: Adventures of a Boy in Vietnam." Decide whether the author used a first-person point of view or a third-person point of view. Then, rewrite the paragraph using the opposite point of view.

1. "My father, like most of the villagers, was a farmer and a hunter, depending upon the season. But he also had a college education, so in the evenings he helped to teach other children in our hamlet, for it was too small to afford a professional schoolteacher."

Point of view: First-person _____

New Paragraph: **Possible Answer** His father, like most of the villagers, was a farmer and a hunter, depending upon the season. But he also had a college education, so in the evenings he helped to teach other children in his hamlet, for it was too small to afford a professional schoolteacher.

_____

Apply **Read each paragraph, and determine whether it is in the first-person or third-person point of view. Then, rewrite the paragraph, using the opposite point of view.**

2. When Shelly moved to a new neighborhood, she was not sure she liked the kids who lived there, but when she got an invitation to her next-door neighbor's birthday party, she made several new friends.

Point of view: third-person

New Paragraph: When I moved to a new neighborhood, I was not sure I would like the kids who lived there, but when I got an invitation to my next-door neighbor's birthday party, I made several new friends.

3. "Never in my wildest dreams did I expect to see you here!" shouted Andy in surprise. I just stood up and smiled. It was good to see Andy after so many months.

Point of view: first-person

New Paragraph: "Never in my wildest dreams did I expect to see you here!" shouted Andy in surprise. His friend stood up and smiled. He was glad to see Andy again after so many months.

Name _____ Date _____

Recording Concept Information

As I read the selection, this is what I added to my understanding of heritage.

- "The Land I Lost: Adventures of a Boy in Vietnam" by Huynh Quang Nhuong

Possible Answer I learned of the importance of preserving one's heritage and remembering family members.

- "Our Song" by Angela Johnson

Possible Answer People can learn a great deal about heritage from their families, even if their lives are very different.

- "The Dancing Bird of Paradise" by Renee S. Sanford

Possible Answer People can keep their cultural traditions alive even through difficult times.

- "From Miss Ida's Porch" by Sandra Belton

Possible Answer Storytelling is a good way for people to learn about their heritage.

- "In Two Worlds: A Yup'ik Eskimo Family" by Aylette Jenness and Alice Rivers

Possible Answer It is important to remember and preserve one's heritage as the world around us changes.

Knowledge about Heritage

- This is what I know about heritage before reading the unit.

Possible Answer Heritage is about your family and ancestors.

It is about traditions like songs and recipes passed down from

generation to generation.

_____

_____

_____

_____

- These are some things about heritage that I would like to talk
  about and understand better.

Possible Answer What is my heritage and how far back does

my family go? How can you learn about heritage if you do not

know what it is?

_____

_____

_____

_____

Reminder: I should read this page again when I get to the
end of the unit to see how much my ideas about heritage
have changed.

Name _____ **Date** _____

Ideas about Heritage

Of the ideas discussed in class about heritage, these are the ones I found most interesting.

Possible Answer Our family is much more than just our

relations. Almost everything about our culture and heritage

filters through our family in the form of stories and habits.

_____

_____

_____

_____

_____

_____

_____

_____

_____

_____

Ideas about Heritage (continued)

Write down the ideas you found most interesting about the selection "The Land I Lost: Adventures of a Boy in Vietnam." Discuss your ideas with the class.

Possible Answer Our heritage makes us individuals while at the same time unifies all of us. We have a heritage that is our own, but we also have a shared heritage with people in our town, our state, our nation, even with everyone in the world.

Name _____ Date _____

Writing a List

**Think**

Audience: Who will read your list?

Possible Answer I will read it. _____

Purpose: What is your reason for making a list? **Possible Answer**
The list will help me brainstorm ideas for a story. _____

Prewriting Using the lines below, brainstorm five topic ideas for a story about an accomplishment of one of your family members. Then, choose one idea and write a pro and a con about using it for your topic.

Possible Answers

Idea #1 My uncle moved to Mexico and became an artist. _____

_____

Idea #2 My mom went back to school so she could become a _____

nurse. _____

Idea #3 My little sister's soccer team just won a tournament. _____

_____

Idea #4 My great-grandparents traveled on a ship from Spain to ____

reach America. _____

Idea #5 My mom gives blood once a month at the clinic where _____

she works. _____

Pro: My uncle paints great pictures of Mexico. _____

_____

Con: I do not know my uncle very well. _____

_____

Revising   Use this checklist to revise your list.

☐ Do the ideas in your list follow the writing assignment?

☐ Have you made a second list of pros and cons for each topic idea?

☐ Have you worked with others, sharing your list to get feedback about your ideas?

☐ Have you decided which suggestions you will follow and which ones you will disregard?

Editing/Proofreading   Use this checklist to correct mistakes.

☐ Are any words misused or repeated?

☐ Have you checked for mistakes in spelling or capitalization?

☐ Have you capitalized proper nouns, literary titles, nationalities, ethnicities, languages, and geographic names and places?

Publishing   Use this checklist to prepare your list for publication.

☐ Brainstorm possible publication methods with your group.

☐ Share your list with the class.

Name _____ Date _____

Spelling

Focus

- **Compound words** consist of two smaller words that have been combined to form one larger word. These two words keep the same spelling in the compound word.

- **Root words** were formed from words of other languages, such as Greek and Latin. Understanding and identifying root words and their meanings can help you spell many new words. Here are some roots in the spelling words and their meanings:

  sol = alone   **scop** = to see   **stella** = star

Word List

1. skateboard
2. rattlesnake
3. mountainside
4. solo
5. telescope
6. peppermint
7. solitary
8. outstanding
9. constellation
10. stellar
11. desolate
12. solitude
13. underground
14. periscope
15. earthquake
16. breakfast
17. scope
18. sweatshirt
19. microscope
20. thunderstorm

Practice The following compound words are missing one of their base words. Write the missing word on the line.

1. _____ rattle snake
2. out standing _____
3. _____ skate board
4. _____ break fast
5. thunder storm _____
6. _____ pepper mint
7. _____ under ground
8. mountain side _____
9. _____ earth quake
10. sweat shirt _____

Fill in the appropriate root word and write the resulting spelling word on the line.

11. _____ sol itary solitary
12. tele _____ scop e telescope
13. con _____ stella tion constellation
14. de _____ sol ate desolate
15. micro _____ scop e microscope
16. _____ sol itude solitude
17. peri _____ scop e periscope
18. _____ sol o solo
19. _____ stella r stellar
20. _____ scop e scope

Apply On the line, write the spelling word that contains one of the base words in the following compound words

21. rainstorm thunderstorm
22. underwater underground
23. surfboard skateboard
24. sideways mountainside
25. outdoors outstanding
26. earthworm earthquake
27. spearmint peppermint
28. shirtsleeves sweatshirt

Name _____ **Date** _____

Common Nouns and Proper Nouns

Focus

Nouns name people, places, or things.

- A **common noun** is used to name a general, or nonspecific, person, place, or thing.
- teacher, library

- A **proper noun** is used to name a particular, or specific, person, place, or thing.
- Ms. Alvarez, Cook County Library

Practice Circle the nouns in the following sentences.

1. For nearly eighty years, Pluto was known as the ninth planet in our solar system.

2. Clyde Tombaugh discovered the tiny frozen sphere in 1930.

3. Recently, though, scientists have decided that Pluto is too small to be labeled a planet.

4. Planets like Earth, Mars, or Jupiter are much larger than Pluto.

5. Pluto is now officially known as a *dwarf* planet.

Apply Each pair of words below should include a common noun followed by a related proper noun. For example, *book* might be followed by *My Side of the Mountain*. Fill in the missing half of each pair below.

Possible Answers

Common Noun	Proper Noun
6. country	France
7. former president	Abraham Lincoln
8. river	Colorado River
9. mountain	Mt. Rainier
10. student	Shelby
11. day	Saturday
12. relative	Uncle Ricardo
13. city	New York
14. school	Southeast High School
15. holiday	Memorial Day

Grammar, Usage, and Mechanics • *Skills Practice 1*

Name _____ Date _____

Prefixes *tele-* and *dis-*

- The prefix **tele-** means "far." Adding *tele-* to a base or root word changes its meaning. For example, *vision* is the ability to see; *television* is the device used to receive images broadcast over long distances.

- The prefix **dis-** means "not" or "the opposite of." Adding *dis-* to a base word often creates an antonym, or a word with the opposite meaning. For example, *disagree* is an antonym for *agree; disadvantage* means the opposite of *advantage.*

Add the prefix *tele-* or the prefix *dis-* to each base word below, and then write the new word's definition on the line. Use a dictionary if you need help.

1. content _discontent_____

Possible Answer not satisfied or pleased _____

2. conference _teleconference_____

Possible Answer a conference among people who are far from one another ___

3. comfort _discomfort_____

Possible Answer a feeling of uneasiness or something disturbing _____

4. communication _telecommunication_____

Possible Answer communication over long distances _____

5. continuous _discontinuous_____

Possible Answer something broken or interrupted _____

Apply Five base or root words and their meanings are given below. Add the prefix *dis-* or the prefix *tele-* to each base or root word, and then use the new word correctly in a sentence. Remember that a word's literal meaning is often different from its actual meaning.

6. connected = joined <u>disconnected</u>

   Possible Answer We disconnected the hose from the faucet.

7. phone = device for transmitting sound <u>telephone</u>

   Possible Answer The telephone is a great way for some people, who live far from one another, to communicate.

8. photo = picture of a person or thing <u>telephoto</u>

   Possible Answer T. J. used a telephoto lens to get close-up pictures of distant objects.

9. scope = extent or range of view <u>telescope</u>

   Possible Answer With his telescope, Nitesh could see the rings of Saturn.

10. approved = agreed to <u>disapproved</u>

   Possible Answer The teacher disapproved of the student's actions.

Name _____ Date _____

Selection Vocabulary

Focus

Senegal (Sen' • i • gôl) *n.* a country in Africa (page 44)

lavender (la' • vən • dər) *n.* a plant with fragrant purple flowers (page 47)

delicate (de' • li • kət) *adj.* small or dainty (page 48)

ship (ship) *v.* to send by ship, train, truck, or airplane (page 50)

traders (trā' • dərz) *n.* plural of **trader:** a person who buys and sells things as a business (page 51)

surrounded (sə • round' • əd) *v.* past tense of **surround:** to be on all sides (page 51)

mist (mist) *n.* a cloud of tiny drops of water or other liquid in the air; fog (page 53)

ignores (ig • norz') *v.* pays no attention to (page 53)

quivers (kwi' • vərz) *v.* shakes slightly (page 54)

Practice **Write the vocabulary word that best matches the underlined word or phrase in each sentence below.**

1. The six of us <u>were on all sides</u> of the kitten as it played with a piece of string. _____surrounded_____

2. A field of <u>fragrant purple flowers</u> filled the countryside with a pleasant scent. _____lavender_____

3. At the toy convention, hundreds of <u>people who buy and sell</u> had set up booths. _____traders_____

4. My dog's entire body <u>shakes slightly</u> when he knows he is about to get a treat. _____quivers_____

5. The patrons were cooled by <u>drops of water in the air</u> drifting from a nearby fountain. _____mist_____

6. We need to <u>send</u> these supplies by airplane, or they will not arrive in time. _____ship_____

7. When the train passes by her apartment, Natalie <u>pays no attention</u> to the noise. _____ignores_____

8. After he bumped the table in the museum, Paul broke the <u>small and dainty</u> vase. _____delicate_____

9. His family is from <u>a country in Africa.</u> _____Senegal_____

Apply | Draw a line to match each word on the left to its definition on the right.

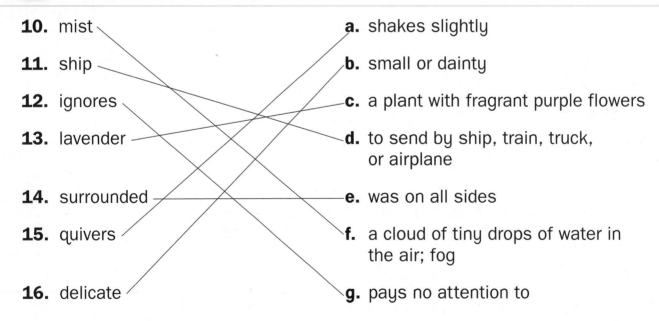

10. mist

11. ship

12. ignores

13. lavender

14. surrounded

15. quivers

16. delicate

a. shakes slightly

b. small or dainty

c. a plant with fragrant purple flowers

d. to send by ship, train, truck, or airplane

e. was on all sides

f. a cloud of tiny drops of water in the air; fog

g. pays no attention to

Name _____ **Date** _____

Formulating Questions and Problems

A good question or problem to investigate:

Possible Answer What is it about my heritage that makes me different from my classmates? What is it that makes us similar?

Why this is an interesting question or problem:

Possible Answer It provides a direct connection to the unit. It is also an opportunity to get to know more about our class and about ourselves.

Some other things I wonder about this question or problem:

Possible Answer Will this help us learn more about our community? Will we be able to make connections between our own personal heritage and our communal heritage?

Formulating Questions and Problems (continued)

My investigation group's question or problem:

Possible Answer What is each group member's family history? Where do the branches of their family tree go? How does this make each member unique? Or do they have a common heritage with others in the group?

What our investigation will contribute to the rest of the class:

Possible Answer This will enable us to get to know each other better as individuals and as a collective group. We will learn more about what makes each of us who we are.

Some other things I wonder about this question or problem:

Possible Answer How does our class compare to our community? Are we the continuance of a long cultural tradition, or does our heritage signal change?

Name _____ Date _____

Writing a Summary: One Text

Think

Audience: Who will read your summary?

Possible Answer I will.

Purpose: What is your reason for writing a summary?

Possible Answer I will use my summary to help my small group summarize "Our Song."

Prewriting Summarizing can help you study by making the text easier to understand. Summaries can also tell others about what you have read. Choose one page from "Our Song," and reread it. On the lines provided, write three ideas or events from the page you chose.

Possible Answers

Page: _____50_____

Idea/Event #1: Josie's "dream cousins" have become real to her.

_____

Idea/Event #2: Josie is given a tour of the village by her cousins.

_____

Idea/Event #3: Josie does not want to wear a hat or shoes.

_____

What is the page's main idea or event?

Josie wants to be like her cousins because she thinks they have a lot of freedom.

On a separate sheet of paper, write a short paragraph summarizing the page you read.

Revising
Use this checklist to revise your summary.

☐ Does your summary have a main idea?

☐ Is your main idea a single sentence that describes the story?

☐ Do your details support the main idea?

☐ Are your details told in an order that makes sense?

Editing/Proofreading
Use this checklist to correct mistakes.

☐ Have you checked the spellings of proper names against the original text?

☐ Have you used correct punctuation for each sentence?

☐ Have you checked for spelling errors?

☐ Have you used correct sentence structure, including subject and predicate?

Publishing
Use this checklist to publish your summary.

☐ Print or neatly rewrite your summary.

☐ Share your summary with the class.

Name _____   Date _____

Spelling

Focus

• A prefix changes the meaning of the base word it precedes. Identifying prefixes and understanding their meanings can help you figure out the meaning and spelling of a difficult or unfamiliar word. The prefix **tele-** means "far," or "at a distance." The prefix **dis-** means "not or not having". It negates the meanings of the base word. These prefixes do not change the spellings of the base words.

• **Root words** were formed from words of other languages, such as Greek and Latin. Understanding and identifying root words and their meanings can help you spell many new words. Here are some roots in the spelling words and their meanings:
graph = write; **imag** = likeness;
phon = sound; **vis** = see; **photo** = light;
gram = letter, written; **nat** = born;
ord or **ordin** = order; rank

Word List

1. disorder
2. telegraph
3. image
4. imagination
5. nationality
6. telephone
7. dishonest
8. television
9. disadvantage
10. disagree
11. telephoto
12. national
13. imagine
14. nation
15. telecast
16. discontinue
17. nationalize
18. telegram
19. imaginary
20. international

Practice

On the lines, write all of the spelling words that contain the same root or base word as each of the following words. Some words will have more than one answer.

1. native   national, nation, nationalize, international, nationality

2. unimaginative
image, imagination, imagine, imaginary

3. autograph

telegraph

4. visual

television

5. grammar

telegram

6. symphony

telephone

7. ordinary

disorder

8. recast

telecast

9. continuation

discontinue

10. agreement

disagree

11. photograph

telephoto

12. advantageous

disadvantage

13. honesty

dishonest

 **Apply**   Add the prefix *tele-* or *dis-* to each of the following base words to create one of the spelling words and write it on the line.

14. gram   telegram

15. cast   telecast

16. order   disorder

17. agree   disagree

18. honest   dishonest

19. continue   discontinue

20. graph   telegraph

21. advantage   disadvantage

22. phone   telephone

Name _____ Date _____

Subjects, Predicates, and Simple Sentences

Focus

A **simple sentence** contains only one independent clause with a subject and a predicate.

- The **subject** is the part of the sentence that tells who or what.

- The **predicate** is the part of the sentence that describes or tells what the subject does.

- A **simple subject** is the key noun or pronoun in a simple sentence that does something or is described.

- A **compound subject** is two or more simple subjects linked by a conjunction.

- The **predicate** in a simple sentence can also be simple or compound.

- **The students** visited a nature preserve.

- The students **visited a nature preserve.**

- The **students** visited a nature preserve.

- The **students** and their **teacher** visited a nature preserve.

- The students **visited a nature preserve** and **had a picnic.**

Practice

The following sentences are simple sentences. Circle the subject and underline the predicate in each sentence.

1. Griots are traveling musicians and poets.

2. They play an important role in West African culture.

3. The history and traditions of West African people were shared by word of mouth for many centuries.

4. The griots' songs and poems helped keep the stories alive.

5. The stories helped preserve the culture's rich heritage.

Apply — Identify the subject and predicate in each sentence below. Then, label each subject *S* for simple or *C* for compound. Do the same for each predicate. Write an *S* next to each sentence that is a simple sentence.

6. _____ Subject: ___C___ Predicate: ___S___
Because they love the sport, Lauren and Jackie play softball every other Saturday.

7. ___S___ Subject: ___S___ Predicate: ___C___
Their team won six games and lost three last year.

8. ___S___ Subject: ___C___ Predicate: ___S___
Mrs. Suarez and her son, Will, have attended every game and several practices.

9. _____ Subject: ___S___ Predicate: ___S___
Because they are polite, they bring sandwiches for everyone after the game.

10. ___S___ Subject: ___S___ Predicate: ___C___
Jackie sprained her ankle and missed two games at the start of this season.

11. ___S___ Subject: ___C___ Predicate: ___C___
She and a team member collided and knocked each other to the ground.

12. ___S___ Subject: ___S___ Predicate: ___S___
Lauren played Jackie's position at first base for the next two games.

Name _____ Date _____

Multiple-Meaning Words, the Prefix *un-*, and the Prefix *en-*

Focus
- **Multiple-meaning words** are words with more than one meaning, but the same word origin. You will often need to look at context clues to figure out which meaning is being used.

- The prefix **un-** means "not or the opposite of." For example, the word *unbalanced* means "not balanced or in disorder."

- The prefix **en-** means "to put into," or "to cause to be." For example, *ensure* means "to cause to be sure."

Practice Each word below uses the prefix *en-* or *un-*. Use your knowledge of the base word's meaning to write an original sentence for each word. Identify the base words that are multiple-meaning words and provide two definitions for each word.

1. *entangle* _____ **Possible Answer** The fish became entangled in the tentacles of the jellyfish.

2. *encircle* _____ **Possible Answer** The river encircles the village. to surround; a sphere, ringlike object or formation

3. *unfair* _____ **Possible Answer** The decision was unfair. a gathering of buyers and sellers for trade, just and impartial

4. *uncomfortable* _____ **Possible Answer** The hard cushions of the couch made it uncomfortable.

Apply The following sentences contain multiple-meaning words. The words and their possible meanings follow the sentence. Circle the letter of the meaning that is used in the sentence. If the prefix *en-* or *un-* can be added to the word, then add the prefix and write the definition of the resulting word on the line.

In the <u>center</u> of the <u>case,</u> there was an emblem representing the owner.

5. center
   (a.) the middle part
   b. a building used for a particular function

_____

6. case
   a. an instance or occurrence
   (b.) small, portable container
   Possible Answer encase: to enclose

_____

Though Tim had a good <u>excuse</u> for his absence, we were still <u>forced</u> to abruptly cancel the event.

7. excuse
   (a.) apology or to try to remove blame from
   b. to allow to leave

_____

8. forced
   (a.) compelled
   b. power or strength
   Possible Answer enforced: imposed upon a person

_____

Name _____   Date _____

Selection Vocabulary

Focus

kimono (ki • mō' • nə) *n.* a loose robe that is tied with a sash (page 64)

phonograph (fō' • nə • graf') *n.* an instrument that reproduces sound from records (page 64)

startled (stär' • tld) *adj.* excited by sudden surprise or alarm (page 66)

internment (in • tûrn' • mənt) *adj.* confined or impounded, especially during a time of war (page 68)

barrack (bar' • ək) *adj.* providing temporary housing; very plain and uniform (page 69)

sweltered (swel' • tərd) *v.* past tense of **swelter:** to suffer, sweat, or become faint from heat (page 69)

ascend (ə • send') *v.* to climb (page 71)

donned (dond) *v.* past tense of **don:** to put on (page 72)

soloed (sōl' • ōd) *v.* past tense of **solo:** to dance or perform alone (page 72)

enrich (en • rich') *v.* to make better by adding something (page 73)

Practice   Circle the word in parentheses that best completes each sentence.

1. My dad replaced his (barrack, (phonograph)) with a CD player years ago.

2. Heather (soloed, (donned)) a hat and gloves before heading out into the cold.

3. The hikers ((sweltered), startled) under the punishing desert sun.

4. The crowd cheered as the guitarist (startled, (soloed)) during the last half of the song.

5. The festival begins when the hot-air balloons ((ascend), enrich) into the sky.

6. A server wearing a (barrack, (kimono)) served us sushi.

7. The sailors were (startled, sweltered) by a sudden wave that crashed against the boat.

8. Julio used slides to (enrich, phonograph) his presentation.

9. The (kimono, barrack) apartments provided shelter for many families escaping the flood.

10. The (internment, startled) camp was the home for many families during World War II.

Apply Write the word from the box that matches each definition below.

barrack	phonograph	donned	ascend	enrich
soloed	kimono	internment	sweltered	startled

11. _____internment_____ confined or impounded

12. _____enrich_____ to make better by adding something

13. _____phonograph_____ an instrument that reproduces sound from records

14. _____sweltered_____ suffered or became faint from heat

15. _____kimono_____ a loose robe that is tied with a sash

16. _____barrack_____ providing very plain temporary housing

17. _____donned_____ put on

18. _____soloed_____ danced or performed alone

19. _____startled_____ excited by sudden surprise

20. _____ascend_____ to climb

Name _____   Date _____

Making Inferences

Writers often do not include every detail about a character or an event in the story. Readers must use clues from the text to make inferences in order to complete the picture. **Making inferences** means using the writer's clues and your own prior knowledge and experiences to develop a better understanding of the character or event.

Practice **Read the following sentences from "The Dancing Bird of Paradise." Make an inference about Sahomi based on each sentence and write it on the line.**

1. "Twenty minutes was all [Sahomi] had alone with her teacher, but she stayed much longer each afternoon, watching and copying the other students, learning their dances as well as her own."

   Inference: **Possible Answer** Sahomi was dedicated and hard-working.

2. "When she taught her students, Sahomi explained the story and meaning behind each dance."

   Inference: **Possible Answer** Sahomi believed that knowing a dance's history was as important as learning its steps.

Apply | Read the description of each character below. Then write a short paragraph inferring how the character feels without actually stating it.

3. a dog who wants to play

Possible Answer Rex bounded into the room, searching for his favorite toy. He found it lying in the corner of the room. Rex grabbed the toy in his mouth and ran over to Sammy. He dropped the toy at Sammy's feet, and then looked up with his tail wagging.

4. a performer who is nervous

Possible Answer Sarah stood at the edge of the stage waiting to go on next. She wrung her hands and looked out at the huge audience. She had never performed before so many people. She closed her eyes and tried to calm down.

5. a boy excited to see his favorite movie

Possible Answer When Johnny heard his favorite movie was showing at the local theatre, he could hardly believe it. He saved his allowance for the entire week to buy his movie ticket. The movie was showing at noon, but Johnny arrived at ten. He wanted to make sure he had a good seat.

Comprehension Skill • *Skills Practice 1*

Name _____ Date _____

Making Conjectures

Our question or problem:

Possible Answer What do immigrants bring with them when they come to a new country?

_____

_____

_____

_____

Conjecture (my first theory or explanation):

_____

Possible Answer Immigrants bring their customs like traditional dances, foods, celebrations, and dress with them.

_____

_____

_____

_____

_____

As you collect information, your conjecture will change. Return to this page to record your new theories or explanations about your question or problem.

Establishing Investigation Needs

My group's question or problem:

Possible Answer What do immigrants bring with them when they come to a new country?

Knowledge Needs—Information I need to find or figure out in order to investigate the question or problem:

A: **Possible Answer** I need to know why they immigrated.

B: **Possible Answer** I need to know where they came from.

C: **Possible Answer** I need to know why their customs are so

D: important to them.

E: _____

Possible Answers

Source	Useful?	How?
Encyclopedias	yes	to show where the immigrants came from
Books	yes	information on immigration
Magazines		
Newspapers		
Video and Audio Clips	yes	program on immigration
Television		
Interviews or observations		
Museums	yes	for graphics, art, and examples of dress
Other:	yes	for information on immigration

Lesson 3

Name _____   Date _____

Writing a Summary: Two Texts

Think

Audience: Who will read your summary?

Possible Answer a classmate _____

Purpose: What is your reason for writing a summary?

Possible Answer I want to tell my readers about two

stories I have read. _____

Prewriting

When summarizing more than one text, you need to show similarities and differences. Comparing details shows what the texts have in common. Contrasting details shows how they are different. Use the organizer to compare and contrast "Our Song" with "The Dancing Bird of Paradise."

Subject 1 Our Song	Similarities	Subject 2 The Dancing Bird of Paradise

Possible Answers

Josie learns a traditional song; Josie is a fictional character; Josie is ten years old throughout the story.

They both live with a grandparent; they both leave America and travel to their grandparents' home country; they both learn about their cultures.

Sahomi learns a traditional dance; Sahomi is a real person; the story follows Sahomi into adulthood.

Write two to three paragraphs summarizing the similarities and differences between the two stories.

Revising
Use this checklist to revise your summary.

☐ Does your summary have a main idea?

☐ Do the details support your main idea?

☐ Did you present your comparisons and contrasts in a logical order?

☐ Do your comparisons and contrasts make sense?

☐ Have you included adjectives and adverbs to make your writing more interesting?

Editing/Proofreading
Use this checklist to correct mistakes.

☐ Are your adjectives and adverbs, including comparatives and superlatives, used correctly?

☐ Have you checked for errors in spelling, capitalization, and punctuation?

☐ Have you read your summary several times to check for mistakes?

Publishing
Use this checklist to share your summary.

☐ Neatly type or rewrite your summary.

☐ Share your summary with someone who might like either of the stories.

Name _____ **Date** _____

Spelling

Focus

A prefix changes the meaning of the base word it precedes. Identifying prefixes and understanding their meanings can help you figure out the meaning and spelling of a difficult or unfamiliar word. Many words feature the prefixes *un-* and *en-*. The prefix **un-** means "not," or "the opposite of." The prefix **en-** has several meanings: "to put in or into"; "to cause to be"; "thoroughly." These prefixes do not change the spelling of the base words.

Word List

1. enrich
2. unpleasant
3. endanger
4. enable
5. uninspired
6. unlikely
7. encompass
8. unmarked
9. enlarge
10. ungrateful
11. encode
12. enlighten
13. unlimited
14. unsatisfied
15. unsweetened
16. enjoy
17. encourage
18. uneaten
19. enrage
20. unnamed

Practice

Add the prefix *un-* or *en-* to the following base words and write the resulting spelling words on the lines.

1. ____named   unnamed
2. ____eaten   uneaten
3. ____joy   enjoy
4. ____satisfied   unsatisfied
5. ____lighten   enlighten
6. ____grateful   ungrateful
7. ____rich   enrich
8. ____danger   endanger
9. ____inspired   uninspired
10. ____compass   encompass

11. _____large   enlarge

12. _____code   encode

13. _____limited   unlimited

14. _____sweetened   unsweetened

15. _____courage   encourage

16. _____rage   enrage

17. _____likely   unlikely

18. _____marked   unmarked

19. _____able   enable

20. _____pleasant   unpleasant

Apply | The following words are misspelled. Write the correctly spelled spelling word on the line. If the word is already correct, write correct.

21. ennamed   unnamed

22. ungrateful   correct

23. enmarked   unmarked

24. unrage   enrage

25. enlarge   correct

26. unjoy   enjoy

27. uncompass   encompass

28. ensatisfied   unsatisfied

29. enlighten   correct

30. unrich   enrich

Name _____ Date _____

Adjectives and Adverbs

Focus   **Adjectives** modify nouns.

- Adjectives show what kind, how many, and which one.
- **colorful** shirts; **several** children

- Proper adjectives, like proper nouns, are always capitalized.
- **French** toast; **Jewish** deli

Adverbs modify verbs, adjectives, and other adverbs.

- Adverbs show how, when, where, and to what extent.
- walked **slowly;** bowled **yesterday;** jumping **around; very** quiet

Practice   Circle the adjectives, and underline the adverbs in the following paragraph.

(Each) spring, Washington, D.C. is filled with the (colorful) blossoms of (Japanese) (cherry) trees. In 1912, (Tokyo's) mayor generously donated (three) (thousand) trees. They clearly symbolized the (growing) friendship between Japan and America. A (two-week) festival is held annually to celebrate the (blossoming) trees and (Japanese) culture.

Apply
Read each numbered sentence. On the first line, write *adjective* or *adverb.* On the second line, write the word or phrase from the box that describes how the adjective or adverb functions in the sentence.

how	what kind	where	to what extent
when	how many	which one	

1. Tom, Shane, and Wylie were **deeply** involved in a **card** game.

   a. *Deeply* is an ___adverb___; it tells ___to what extent___.

   b. *Card* is an ___adjective___; it tells ___what kind___.

2. They **always** relaxed in Shane's **tree** house when it was **too** hot to play basketball.

   a. *Always* is an ___adverb___; it tells ___when___.

   b. *Tree* is an ___adjective___; it tells ___what kind___.

   c. *Too* is an ___adverb___; it tells ___to what extent___.

3. **Suddenly,** a **loud** crash echoed through Shane's **normally** calm backyard.

   a. *Suddenly* is an ___adverb___; it tells ___how___.

   b. *Loud* is an ___adjective___; it tells ___what kind___.

   c. *Normally* is an ___adverb___; it tells ___to what extent___.

4. The **two** boys **carefully** climbed **down** from the tree house.

   a. *Two* is an ___adjective___; it tells ___how many___.

   b. *Carefully* is an ___adverb___; it tells ___how___.

   c. *Down* is an ___adverb___; it tells ___where___.

Name _____ Date _____

Suffixes *-ant*, *-y*, and *-ity*

Focus The suffix **-ant** means "being in a particular state" or "one who does something." For example, adding the suffix *-ant* to the word *serve* changes it to *servant,* or "one who serves."

The suffix **-y** means "having the quality of, state." For example, someone who has *luck* is *lucky.*

The suffix **-ity** means, "the quality or condition of." The suffix converts certain adjectives into nouns. For example, something that is *necessary* is a *necessity.*

Practice **Complete each sentence below with a word that uses the suffix *-ant*.**

1. Someone who assists is an _____assistant_____.

2. Someone who immigrates is an _____immigrant_____.

3. Someone who occupies a room is an _____occupant_____.

4. Someone who inhabits a place is an _____inhabitant_____.

5. Someone who sells merchandise is a _____merchant_____.

Complete each sentence below with a word that uses the suffix *-y* or *-ity*.

6. Something that has the quality of being fun is _____funny_____.

7. Something that is real represents _____reality_____.

8. Something that is considered abnormal is an _____abnormality_____.

9. When the sun is shining outside it is _____sunny_____.

10. Someone who is civil has _____civility_____.

Apply Read the following root words and their definitions.
Use each root to create a word that ends with the
suffix in parentheses, and then use the new word in a sentence.
Use a dictionary if you need help.

11. vac = empty (-ant)

Possible Answer The house next door was vacant for

nearly a year.

12. gust = sudden burst (-y)

Possible Answer The gusty winds caught us by surprise,

and the umbrella blew away.

13. dorm = sleep (-ant)

Possible Answer The dormant volcano began rumbling

to life.

14. bulk = large in size (-y)

Possible Answer The bulky load was almost too much for

the ox to carry.

15. defy = challenge (-ant)

Possible Answer Audrey had a defiant look on her face as

she defended her little brother.

16. able = having skill to accomplish a task (-ity)

Possible Answer He had the ability to be a great dancer.

Name _____ Date _____

Selection Vocabulary

Focus

attitude (at' • ə • tōōd') *n.* a way of acting, thinking, or feeling (page 84)

claim (klām) *v.* to declare as one's own (page 85)

magnificent (mag • ni' • fə • sənt) *adj.* outstanding; excellent (page 85)

spellbound (spel' • bound) *adj.* fascinated; filled with delight or wonder (page 86)

civilizations (si' • və • lə • zā' • shənz) *n.* plural of **civilization**: an advanced human society in which agriculture, trade, government, art, and science are highly developed (page 86)

section (sek' • shən) *n.* a part of an area (page 87)

concert (kon' • sûrt') *n.* a musical performance (page 87)

finest (fī' • nəst) *adv.* best; most excellent (page 88)

forbidden (fər • bi' • dən) *adj.* off-limits (page 88)

trolley (trol' • ē) *n.* a streetcar that runs on tracks and gets its power from an electric wire overhead (page 90)

Practice   Write the word from the Focus box that best fits each clue.

1. It is one part of a building, a city, or any other area.

What is it? _____ section _____

2. The Egyptians and the Mayans had famous ones.

What are they? _____ civilizations _____

3. It is the best ice cream you have ever eaten.

Which word compares it to other ice creams? _____ finest _____

4. A positive one is always better than a negative one.

What is it? _____ attitude _____

5. This musical event can take place in an auditorium or a stadium.

What is it? _____ concert _____

6. During the most dramatic part of a movie, your mouth hangs open, and you do not want to blink.

What are you? _____ spellbound _____

7. Clang! Clang! Clang! Next stop, Telegraph Hill!

Where might you hear this? _____ trolley _____

8. Do not enter! Stop! You are not allowed inside!

What kind of place would have these messages? _____ forbidden _____

9. A lost glove waits quietly in a Lost and Found box.

What does it need someone to do to it? _____ claim _____

10. Critics love it! Audiences agree. It is an excellent film.

What word describes this movie? _____ magnificent _____

Apply **Select the word that completes each sentence.**

11. The auditorium was filled with _____ magnificent _____ decorations.

12. The front _____ section _____ of our yard has been dug up.

13. Keiko was _____ spellbound _____ as she watched the magician.

14. To succeed in life, it is helpful to have a good _____ attitude _____.

15. Mr. Pérez's bakery makes the _____ finest _____ bread in town.

16. You cannot _____ claim _____ that book because the library owns it.

Describing an Object

Name _____ **Date** _____

Think

Audience: Who will read your description?

Possible Answer another student

Purpose: What do you want your description to do?

Possible Answer I want the reader to be able to clearly picture the objects I have described.

Prewriting

Close your eyes and visualize the object you want to describe. This method will help you focus on the most important details. Use the following graphic organizer to plan your description.

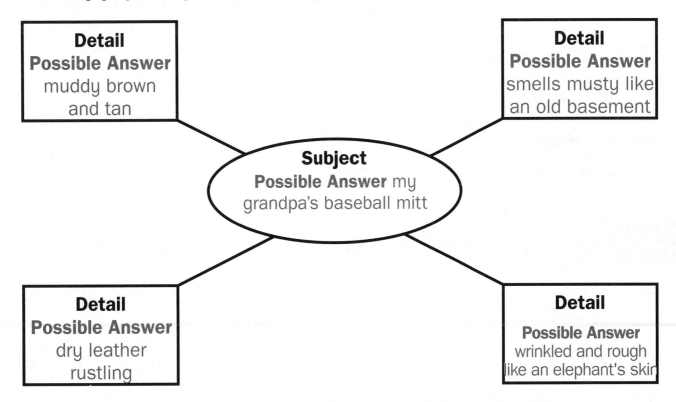

Detail
Possible Answer muddy brown and tan

Detail
Possible Answer smells musty like an old basement

Subject
Possible Answer my grandpa's baseball mitt

Detail
Possible Answer dry leather rustling

Detail
Possible Answer wrinkled and rough like an elephant's skin

Revising
Use this checklist to revise your description.

☐ Are your details grouped in a way that makes sense?

☐ Have you chosen vivid and descriptive words so your reader can identify your object?

☐ Have you used sensory language or figurative language, such as similes and metaphors?

Editing/Proofreading
Use this checklist to edit your description.

☐ Did you use commas and other punctuation correctly?

☐ Have you checked your description for capitalization or spelling errors?

☐ Have you read through your description several times to check for mistakes?

☐ Start making a list of the errors you are commonly making.

Publishing
Use this checklist to publish your description.

☐ Neatly rewrite your final copy in cursive handwriting.

☐ Post your description and illustration in the classroom.

Name _____   Date _____

Spelling

Focus

- Understanding and identifying suffixes and their meanings can help you determine the meaning and spelling of a difficult or unfamiliar word. Many words feature the suffixes *-y, -ity,* and *-ant.*
- The suffix **-y** means "having the quality of, state or condition."
- The suffix **-ity** means "state or quality of."
- The suffix **-ant** means "one who" when added to a verb to make a noun. It means "being in a particular state" or "one that does a particular action or promotes a particular state" when added to a word to make it an adjective.

Word List

1. modesty
2. vigilant
3. servant
4. necessity
5. civility
6. honesty
7. nobility
8. assistant
9. immigrant
10. lucky
11. messy
12. agility
13. rainy
14. pleasant
15. hostility
16. defiant
17. tasty
18. resistant
19. purity
20. formality

Practice Write the spelling word that results when the suffix *-ity, -ant,* or *-y* is added to the following base words or word parts.

1. formal   formality
2. necess   necessity
3. agile   agility
4. noble   nobility
5. hostile   hostility
6. civil   civility
7. pure   purity
8. resist   resistant

Skills Practice 1 • Spelling

9. vigil   vigilant

10. please   pleasant

11. assist   assistant

12. serve   servant

13. immigrate   immigrant

14. defy   defiant

15. taste   tasty

16. rain   rainy

17. modest   modesty

18. luck   lucky

19. honest   honesty

20. mess   messy

 **Apply**   **Correct the misspelled words and write them on the line. If the word is already correct, write correct.**

21. servent   servant

22. honestty   honesty

23. nobilty   nobility

24. assistant   correct

25. pureity   purity

26. formalty   formality

27. modestity   modesty

28. messy   correct

Name _____ Date _____

Commas

Focus **Commas** are used to organize the thoughts and items in a sentence. They show the reader where to pause so that a sentence's meaning can be clearly understood.

- Use a comma to separate three or more items.

- I eat bananas**,** apples**,** and oranges.

- Use a comma after long introductory phrases or dependent clauses.

- **After we finished cleaning the house,** my dad and I relaxed.

- Use a comma and a conjunction to join two independent clauses.

- Luiz wants to play chess**, but** Shonda wants to play checkers.

- Use a comma when an interjection is not followed by an exclamation point.

- **Gosh,** I did not know that. **Hi,** Mr. Harris.

- Use a comma before and after an appositive.

- My friend**, Lacy,** is going to Kentucky.

Practice The commas are missing or used incorrectly in the following sentences. On a separate sheet of paper, rewrite each sentence so that it is correct.

1. During our trip, to Texas we will drive through Tennessee, and Arkansas.
During our trip to Texas, we will drive through Tennessee and Arkansas.
2. Hildy put on, a coat a hat a scarf and mittens and, then she went outside.
Hildy put on a coat, a hat, a scarf, and mittens, and then she went outside.
3. Well that is a great story but, I am not sure I believe it.
Well, that is a great story, but I am not sure I believe it.
4. After five years, in college John my cousin is, about to graduate.
After five years in college, John, my cousin, is about to graduate.
5. We washed dried and peeled, the potatoes, before cutting them into small pieces.   We washed, dried, and peeled the potatoes before cutting them into small pieces.

Apply   **Insert commas where they are needed in the following paragraph.**

W. E. B. DuBois, an important American civil rights leader, was also a writer, poet, editor, and historian. DuBois graduated from Harvard University in 1890, and then he studied in Europe for a few years. After returning to the United States, DuBois became the first black man to earn a Ph.D. from Harvard. DuBois' most famous book, *The Souls of Black Folk*, was published in 1903. He was also a founding member of the NAACP, or the National Association for the Advancement of Colored People. When DuBois died in 1963, he was a citizen of Ghana, a country in Africa.

Name _____ Date _____

Suffixes -ence and -ly and the Inflectional Ending -ing

Focus

- The suffix **-ence** means "state or quality of being." For example, *innocence* means "the quality of being innocent."

- When **-ing** is added to a verb, it forms the present participle. It can be used as a verb, adjective, or noun.

    I saw my friend **running** down the street. (participle)

    Running is good exercise. (noun)

    I bought a pair of **running** shoes. (adjective)

- The suffix **–ly** means "like or resembling." When added to a root or base word the suffix forms adjectives, as in *lovely,* or adverbs, as in *beautifully.*

Practice

Each sentence below contains a boldfaced word with one of the suffixes covered in this lesson. On the line, write *P* if the word is an adverb, *N* if it is a noun, or *A* if it is an adjective.

1. ____A____ Maurice uses a **shopping** cart when he goes to the store.

2. ____P____ I **slowly** licked the ice cream melting down the side of the cone.

3. ____A____ Sometimes Mr. Harrera uses a **sliding** scale to grade papers.

4. ____N____ The Fourth of July is a celebration of America's **independence.**

5. ____A____ You could still see the **dissolving** salt in the liquid.

6. ____N____ Before the trial, the defendant proclaimed his **innocence.**

Apply Complete the "word-math" problems below. Then use each solution in a sentence.

7. evident + ence = <u>evidence</u>

Possible Answer <u>The detective found evidence that</u> <u>helped solve the crime.</u>

8. unusual + ly = <u>unusually</u>

Possible Answer <u>I found an unusually large flower</u> <u>growing in the woods.</u>

9. nurse + ing = <u>nursing</u>

Possible Answer <u>One career I have considered is nursing.</u>

10. selfish + ly = <u>selfishly</u>

Possible Answer <u>My brother acted selfishly when he</u> <u>would not share his candy.</u>

11. comical + ly = <u>comically</u>

Possible Answer <u>Tom speaks comically whenever he</u> <u>wants to get a laugh.</u>

12. sail + ing = <u>sailing</u>

Possible Answer <u>Sailing is my favorite pastime.</u>

Name _____ **Date** _____

Selection Vocabulary

Focus

vast (vast) *adj.* great in size (page 101)

tilted (tilt' • ed) *v.* past tense of **tilt:** to raise one side of (page 101)

withered (with' • ərd) *v.* past tense of **wither:** to dry up from a loss of moisture (page 101)

inhabit (in • ha' • bət) *v.* to live in or on (page 103)

role (rōl) *n.* a position or function (page 109)

luxury (lug' • shoo • rē) *adj.* expensive (page 109)

freighter (frā' • tər) *n.* a ship used for carrying cargo (page 110)

sewage (soo' • ij) *n.* waste that is carried off in sewers and drains (page 111)

lagoon (lə • goon') *n.* a shallow body of water usually connected to a larger body of water (page 111)

fluent (floo' • ənt) *adj.* able to speak effortlessly (page 113)

Practice Write *T* in the blank if the sentence for the vocabulary word is correct. Write *F* if the sentence is false. For every *F* answer, write the word that fits the definition.

1. A freighter is a ship for carrying cargo. T _____

2. A luxury car would be expensive.
T _____

3. To inhabit means "to live in or on something."
T _____

4. A lagoon is a function or a position. F role _____

5. Sewage is waste that is carried off in sewers or drains.

  T _____

6. Fluent means "very great in size or number." F vast _____

7. Withered means "raised one side of." F tilted _____

8. A lagoon is a shallow body of water connected to a larger one.

  T _____

9. One who is vast in a language can speak it effortlessly.

  F fluent _____

10. Withered leaves are dried up from a loss of moisture.

  T _____

 **Apply** **Circle the correct letter to answer each question below.**

11. Which is an example of a *role*?
    (a.) the principal
    b. the filing cabinet

12. Which is an example of something that is *tilted*?
    a. a table with books on it
    (b.) a table on which balls always roll off one side

13. Which is an example of *inhabit*?
    (a.) the birds living in the tree
    b. the birds catching insects as they fly

14. Which is an example of something you would find in a *lagoon*?
    (a.) a rowboat
    b. a car

Name _____ Date _____

Compare and Contrast

Writers compare and contrast to paint a clearer picture of the people and things they are writing about.

- To **compare** means to tell how things, ideas, events, or characters are alike.

- To **contrast** means to tell how things, ideas, events, or characters are different.

Practice Look through "In Two Worlds: A Yup'ik Eskimo Family," and contrast the Scammon Bay of Mary Ann's childhood and the Scammon Bay of today.

1. In Mary Ann's time: **Possible Answer** There were few people living in Scammon Bay, and they moved when the seasons changed in order to catch animals for food to survive.

   Today: **Possible Answer** There are 350 people living in fifty-six houses in Scammon Bay, and they catch fish and sell them for money.

2. In Mary Ann's time: **Possible Answer** They lived in sod houses with mud floors and used seal oil in lamps for light. She was fifteen years old when she first saw an airplane.

   Today: **Possible Answer** A dish antenna provides television to all homes, satellite transmission provides telephone services, and small planes fly to Scammon Bay.

Apply   **Read each sentence, and determine whether it shows a comparison or a contrast. Then, rewrite each sentence reflecting the other term.**

3. Dave and Ed both finished all their vegetables. comparison

Possible Answer Dave finished his vegetables, but Ed did not.

4. Martha plays the trombone, while Janet plays the cello. contrast

Possible Answer Both Martha and Janet play the cello.

5. I like to read mysteries just like my sister Gina. comparison

Possible Answer Unlike my sister Gina, I like to read mysteries.

6. Both cats and dogs make good pets. comparison

Possible Answer Cats make good pets, but dogs are hard to care for.

7. Jacob and Jason are twins, but Jacob is slightly taller. contrast

Possible Answer Jacob and Jason are identical twins.

On a separate sheet of paper, write a paragraph comparing and contrasting yourself to a friend or relative. Be sure to include ways that you are similar and ways that you are different.

Name _____ Date _____

Magazine Articles

Think

Audience: Who will read your magazine article?

Possible Answer my family

Purpose: What is your reason for writing a magazine article?

Possible Answer I want to tell readers about an important event from my family's history.

Prewriting **Magazine articles tell their readers about important events. The information in an article needs to be accurate and complete. Journalists use the following six questions to make sure their stories include all of the facts. Answer the questions to make sure your article will be accurate and complete.**

What happened? **Possible Answer** My great-great-great-grandparents moved to America.

Where did it happen? **Possible Answer** They arrived at Ellis Island before moving to Boston.

Who was involved? **Possible Answer** Patrick and Anna Moore, and their daughter Mildred

When did it happen? **Possible Answer** They arrived here in the 1890s.

Why did it happen? **Possible Answer** Patrick's brother had come to America earlier and encouraged them to follow him.

How did it happen? **Possible Answer** They traveled on a crowded ship across the Atlantic.

Revising
Use this checklist to revise your draft.

☐ Have you varied the introductory phrases in your sentences so that your article does not sound repetitive?

☐ Have you varied sentence types to create rhythm and interest?

☐ Does your opening paragraph grab the reader's attention with an interesting lead?

☐ Have you used descriptive words?

Editing/Proofreading
Use this checklist to look for mistakes in your draft.

☐ Have you spelled proper nouns consistently throughout the article?

☐ Have you checked the events in your story against the time line that you made?

☐ Have you checked your facts more than once?

Publishing
Use this checklist to share your draft.

☐ Have a friend or classmate read your draft.

☐ Listen carefully to his or her suggestions, and decide which ones you will use.

Name _____   **Date** _____

Spelling

Focus Understanding and identifying suffixes and their meanings can help you determine the meaning and spelling of a difficult or unfamiliar word. The suffix *-ly* changes an adjective into an adverb. It means "like or resembling." When the suffix *-ly* changes a noun to an adjective, it means "resembling." It rarely changes the spelling of the base word to which it is added. The suffix *-ence* means "state or quality of," and, when added to a word, makes the word a noun.

Word List
1. independence
2. finally
3. convenience
4. wisely
5. violence
6. timidly
7. absence
8. cautiously
9. turbulence
10. silently
11. emergence
12. desperately
13. excellence
14. accurately
15. difference
16. strictly
17. reference
18. beautifully
19. competence
20. directly

Practice Drop the suffix *-ly* from each word and write the resulting word on the line.

1. finally   final
2. wisely   wise
3. timidly   timid
4. cautiously   cautious
5. silently   silent
6. desperately   desperate
7. accurately   accurate
8. strictly   strict
9. beautifully   beautiful
10. directly   direct

On the line, write the spelling word that results when the suffix *-ence* is added to the following base words or word parts.

11. compete   competence

12. absent   absence

13. convenient   convenience

14. turbulent   turbulence

15. emerge   emergence

16. excel   excellence

17. refer   reference

18. independent   independence

19. violent   violence

20. differ   difference

Apply Select the correct word from the parentheses that completes each sentence and write it on the line.

21. The little boy smiled timidly (timid, timidly) at the doctor.

22. She sang the song beautifully. (beautiful, beautifully)

23. The dog cautiously (cautious, cautiously) sniffed the air before going outside.

24. The students read the book silently. (silently, silence)

25. The town sheriff strictly (strict, strictly) enforced the law.

26. They tried desperately (desperate, desperately) to save the man's life.

Name _____ **Date** _____

Verbs, Verb Phrases, and Objects

Focus

- **Verbs** are words that show action or express a state of being.

- **Verb phrases** consist of one or more helping verbs used with an action or state-of-being verb.

- **Direct objects** are nouns and pronouns that receive the action of the verb.

- **Indirect objects** are nouns and pronouns for or to whom something is done.

- **Objects** are also the nouns and pronouns that appear in prepositional phrases.

- Malcolm **grew** tomatoes and peppers.
  Tomorrow **is** the last day of school.

- I **have picked** a book for my report.
  She **could see** the deer running.

- Pilar finished her **homework**.
  The artist sculpted a **statue**.

- Denzel told his **classmates** a joke.
  We made our **mother** dinner.

- Take me to the **mall**.
  The bird flew over my **head**.

Practice

In the following sentences, circle the verb or verb phrase, and underline the direct object(s) once and the indirect object(s) twice.

1. Natalie (waited) inside the cab.

2. Sometimes our garbage (smells) like rotten eggs.

3. Next year I (will read) Tom Sawyer.

4. The astronauts (could see) Earth from outer space.

5. The pitcher (threw) the batter a curve ball.

6. The concert (was held) near an old, abandoned factory.

7. Soon my order (will arrive) by special delivery.

8. Omar (drew) his friend a picture of some horses.

Apply

The verb or verb phrase in each sentence below has been boldfaced. On the first line, write *A* if it is an action verb or *S* if it is a state-of-being verb. One object in each sentence has also been boldfaced. On the second line, write *D* if it is a direct object, *I* if it is an indirect object, or *P* if it is the object of the preposition.

9. Verb: _____A_____   Object: _____D_____
The bus **carries students** to and from school every day.

10. Verb: _____S_____   Object: _____P_____
I **have been** sick with the **flu** for almost a week.

11. Verb: _____A_____   Object: _____D_____
Lina **sold** Enrique her old **watch.**

12. Verb: _____S_____   Object: _____P_____
The violinist **seemed** satisfied with her **performance.**

13. Verb: _____A_____   Object: _____I_____
Mr. Lin **has told Maxwell** a story about his childhood.

14. Verb: _____A_____   Object: _____D_____
John **understood** the **rules** before he began playing the game.

Name _____ Date _____

Compound Words and the Prefix *in-*

Focus
- **Compound words** are words formed by combining two or more smaller words into one larger word. If you know the smaller words' meanings, you can often figure out the meaning of the compound. For example, a *backpack* is a pack you carry on your back.
- The prefix **in-** means "not," "lacking," or "lack of." Adding *in-* to a base word usually creates a word with the opposite meaning. For example, *incorrect* means "not correct," or the opposite of *correct.*

Practice On the lines below, write definitions for each pair of words. Then write a definition for the compound word they form. Use a dictionary if you need help.

1. saw: **Possible Answer** a device used for cutting wood _____

dust: **Possible Answer** fine dirt or residue made of tiny particles

sawdust: **Possible Answer** dust that is produced when wood is cut

2. head: **Possible Answer** part of the body that holds the brain _____

ache: **Possible Answer** soreness or pain _____

headache: **Possible Answer** having soreness or pain in the head

3. hand: **Possible Answer** part of the body with five fingers _____

made: **Possible Answer** created or designed _____

handmade: **Possible Answer** created by hand

Add the prefix *in-* to the following words and use a dictionary to define each word.

4. difference   <u>indifference</u>

5. direct   <u>indirect</u>

6. dependent   <u>independent</u>

 **Add the prefix *in-* to each word below, and then use the new word in a sentence. Include the compound word listed in your sentence.**

7. <u>in</u>complete — sandcastle

Possible Answer The sandcastle was still incomplete when a wave washed it away.

8. <u>in</u>direct — landmarks

Possible Answer We took an indirect route to Nashville so that we could see some historic landmarks.

9. <u>in</u>convenient — homework

Possible Answer It is inconvenient for me to come by your house after my homework is done.

10. <u>in</u>active — underground

Possible Answer The volcano had been inactive underground for many years before it finally erupted again.

Name _____ Date _____

Selection Vocabulary

Focus

dissolve (di • zolv') *v.* to mix into liquid (page 138)

retirement (ri • tīr' • mənt) *n.* the act of taking oneself away from a job or occupation (page 139)

inefficient (in' • ə • fish' • ənt) *adj.* not offering a good use of money or effort (page 139)

vents (vents) *n.* plural of **vent:** an opening through which a gas passes (page 139)

charged (chärjd) *v.* past tense of **charge:** to fill with electricity (page 141)

demonstration (de' • mən • strā' • shən) *n.* something that explains, proves, or shows something clearly (page 141)

donors (dō' • nərs) *n.* plural of **donor:** a person who gives something (page 142)

electrocuted (i • lek' • trə • kyo͞ot' • əd) *v.* past tense of **electrocute:** to kill by means of a very strong electric shock (page 143)

attracted (ə • trak' • təd) *v.* past tense of **attract:** to cause to come near (page 144)

insulators (in' • sə • lā' • tərz) *n.* plural of **insulator:** a material that does not carry an electric charge (page 144)

Practice **Fill in each blank with the vocabulary word that best completes the sentence.**

1. Mr. Flores gave a ___demonstration___ of how to perform CPR.

2. Delivering one pizza at a time would be an ___inefficient___ way to work.

3. With help from several ___donors___, the Debate Club purchased a new podium.

4. My grandma's **retirement** has given her more time for volunteering.

5. That new bird seed **attracted** nearly a dozen yellow finches to our backyard.

6. **Dissolve** the salt in the water before you add the yeast.

7. DeShawn **charged** his cell phone's battery before leaving for work.

8. Dryer **vents** carry warm, damp air outdoors.

9. The **insulators** covering the wires were necessary to protect the workers working on the electric line from being **electrocuted**.

Apply
Write the vocabulary word that matches each definition below.

10. **vents** — openings through which gases pass

11. **demonstration** — something that explains a process

12. **insulators** — materials that do not carry electrical charges

13. **attracted** — caused to come near

14. **donors** — people who give

15. **dissolve** — to mix into liquid

16. **charged** — filled with electricity

17. **electrocuted** — killed by a strong electric shock

18. **inefficient** — not offering a good use of money or effort

Vocabulary • *Skills Practice 1*

Name _____ Date _____

Recording Concept Information

As I read the selection, this is what I added to my understanding of energy at work.

- "The Sparks Fly" by Ruth Ashby

  Possible Answer I learned that Benjamin Franklin invented many things, but his work with electricity is his most recognized accomplishment.

- "Tailing Tornadoes" by Trudi Strain Trueit

  Possible Answer I learned that the central U.S. is known as Tornado Alley. Energy takes many forms, and tornados and storms are one type.

- "Jake Drake Know-It-All" by Andrew Clements

  Possible Answer I learned that the scientific method is used to prove a hypothesis right or wrong. Electromagnets are another form of energy.

- "The Wind at Work" by Gretchen Woelfle

  Possible Answer I learned that people have always used wind energy to make their lives easier. Alternative energy sources will help to decrease the use of fossil fuels.

- "What are Food Chains and Webs?" by Bobbie Kalman

  Possible Answer I learned that food is another form of energy and that plants and animals are dependent upon one another to survive.

Knowledge about Energy at Work

- This is what I know about energy at work before reading the unit.

  Possible Answer All living things have energy. Food is energy in the form of calories. Electric cars are an example of an alternative fuel source which is cleaner than burning fossil fuels.

  _____

  _____

- These are some things about energy at work that I would like to talk about and understand better.

  Possible Answer What are alternative forms of energy? Why do we not use more of them? How will the car change in the next 25 years? How will my daily energy use change in the next 25 years?

  _____

  _____

  Reminder: I should read this page again when I get to the end of the unit to see how much my ideas about energy at work have changed.

Name _____ **Date** _____

Ideas about Energy at Work

Of the ideas discussed in class about energy at work, these are the ones I found most interesting.

Possible Answer Benjamin Franklin was not only an active writer and politician, but he was a thoughtful scientist as well.

_____

_____

_____

_____

_____

_____

_____

_____

_____

_____

_____

Ideas about Energy at Work (continued)

Write down the ideas you found most interesting about the selection "The Sparks Fly." Discuss your ideas with the class.

Possible Answer Nature and energy can be tracked through science, but they still can be unpredictable and dangerous. This lesson demonstrates the importance of people like Benjamin Franklin, who advanced our understanding of electricty and energy.

Name _____ Date _____

Science Observation Report

 **Audience: Who** will read the report of your experiment?
Possible Answer another student

Purpose: What is your reason for conducting an experiment?
Possible Answer I want to find out whether my

hypothesis is correct or incorrect.

 **It is important to follow the steps of the scientific process. Use the lines below to begin your experiment.**

Problem: **Possible Answer** Does water alone make iron rust?

Hypothesis: **Possible Answer** Water makes iron rust, but iron also needs air to rust.

Procedure: **Possible Answer** I used five glass jars of the same size and iron nails

about 2½ centimeters long and ½ centimeter in diameter, with the head about

1 centimeter in diameter. In Jar 1, I placed two nails in one ounce of water, uncovered.

In Jar 2, I also placed two nails uncovered in one ounce of water. I placed two nails

coated in clear nail polish at the bottom of one ounce of water in Jar 3. I did the same

for Jar 4, except only one nail was coated with polish. In Jar 5, I placed two nails that

were each half coated with nail polish into one ounce of water, uncovered.

The final step in your experiment is to draw conclusions based on your observations. Do your observations support your hypothesis? Write a paragraph summarizing your conclusions.

Revising

Use this checklist to revise the report of your experiment.

☐ Have you referred to data and included your observations?

☐ Have you included all of your observations?

☐ Have you presented the steps of the scientific process in their proper order?

☐ Did you use transition words to show the sequence of events?

☐ Have you varied your sentence type and length so your report is interesting to read?

Editing/Proofreading

Use this checklist to correct mistakes.

☐ Have you labeled the steps of the scientific process correctly?

☐ Did you check all capitalization, punctuation, and spelling?

☐ Have you read your report more than once to check for correctly applied rules for regular and irregular plurals?

Publishing

Use this checklist to publish your results.

☐ Rewrite your report neatly, or type it on a computer.

☐ The final step in the scientific process is to share the results of your experiment with others. For example, you could read your report to the class.

Name _____   **Date** _____

Spelling

Focus

• **Compound words** consist of two smaller words that have been combined to form one larger word. These two words keep the same spelling in the compound word.

• The prefix **in-** has several meanings. It means "not"; or it can mean "within," "into," or "on."

Practice   **Combine the two smaller words to make a compound word from the word list and write it on the line.**

1. news + break = _newsbreak_

2. double + header = _doubleheader_

3. head + quarters = _headquarters_

4. key + board = _keyboard_

5. wind + shield = _windshield_

Add the prefix _in-_ to the following base words to form words from the spelling list and write them on the lines.

6. finite _infinite_

7. accurate _inaccurate_

8. experienced _inexperienced_

9. efficient _inefficient_

10. justice _injustice_

Word List

1. indefinite
2. doubleheader
3. eyewitness
4. inefficient
5. inaccurate
6. windshield
7. loudspeaker
8. undertake
9. headquarters
10. inexperienced
11. keyboard
12. infinite
13. inability
14. injustice
15. grasshopper
16. overindulge
17. insight
18. involuntary
19. newsbreak
20. inconsiderate

Apply On the line, write the spelling word from the list that best fits each definition.

21. a breaking news story _____ newsbreak

22. a board with keys on it _____ keyboard

23. a witness who sees something firsthand _____ eyewitness

24. an insect that hops over the grass _____ grasshopper

25. to indulge too much _____ overindulge

26. a double set of games played one after the other _____ doubleheader

27. a speaker that makes your voice loud and easily heard _____ loudspeaker

28. the place where the head part of a company has its quarters _____ headquarters

29. part of a car that shields you from the wind _____ windshield

30. to take on something, such as a new project _____ undertake

Use the following phrases and select the spelling word that fits the description best. Write the word on the line.

31. not experienced _____ inexperienced

32. not efficient _____ inefficient

33. not voluntary _____ involuntary

34. without ability _____ inability

35. the opposite of justice _____ injustice

36. not considerate _____ inconsiderate

37. seeing into _____ insight

38. not definite _____ indefinite

39. not accurate _____ inaccurate

40. not ending _____ infinite

Name _____ Date _____

Action Verbs

- **Action verbs** add energy and precision to sentences. The action of the verbs can express mental or physical action.
- I **understand** what you are saying.
- Action verbs can be the main verbs in verb phrases.
- Ted has been **thinking** it over.
- Action verbs can also be found in dependent clauses.
- I was relieved when Jen **asked** for help. It was cold because someone **opened** a door.

Practice Circle the action verbs in the paragraph below.

Last week, our class (visited) the Science Museum. We (saw) several demonstrations that (used) electricity. My friend Lana was a volunteer in one of them. Her long hair (stood) up on end when a wand was (waved) over her head. Later, she (told) me that she (knew) what would (happen) because she had been to the museum before. I (hope) that next time I can (volunteer) for that experiment!

Apply Write a sentence that contains an action verb for each noun listed below. Then, underline the action verbs in your sentences.

1. trees

Possible Answer The trees <u>swayed</u> in a strong breeze.

2. baseball

Possible Answer I <u>threw</u> the baseball to the catcher.

3. bus driver

Possible Answer Our bus driver <u>smiles</u> and <u>says</u> hello as each student <u>boards</u>.

4. light bulb

Possible Answer The light bulb <u>burned</u> out soon after we <u>installed</u> it.

5. magazine

Possible Answer My magazine subscription <u>expired</u> last month.

6. freeway

Possible Answer Freeway traffic <u>slowed</u> to a halt because of an accident.

Name _____ Date _____

Word Origins

Recognizing and understanding **word origins** can help you understand new and unfamiliar words. For example, take the word *microscopic.* It contains the Greek root *scop.* This root means "to look at." The prefix *micro-* means "very small." Thus *microscopic* means "too small to be seen."

The following words originate from the same language. They each contain a Latin root that has been defined for you. On the line, write a different word that uses the same root.

1. liberate

Latin root *liber* means, "to free":

Possible Answers

liberty, liberally

2. portable

Latin root *port* means "carry":

Possible Answers

import, transportation

3. reform

Latin root *form* means "shape":

Possible Answers

transform, uniform

4. prediction

Latin root *dic* means, "speak":

Possible Answers

dictate, dictionary

5. abrupt

Latin root *rupt* means, "to break":

Possible Answers

erupt, interrupt

Apply The words below are Greek in origin. The meanings of their roots, prefixes, and suffixes have been provided for you. Define each word based on the meanings of its parts. Check your answers in a dictionary.

6. the prefix *pro-* = in front of

Greek root *logue* = word

prologue = **Possible Answer** words at the beginning of a text

7. the prefix *dia-* = across or through

Greek root *meter* = measure

diameter = **Possible Answer** measurement across a circle

8. Greek root *path* = disease or illness

the suffix *-ology* = study or science of

pathology = **Possible Answer** the study of diseases

9. the prefix *syn-* = together

Greek root *chron* = time

the suffix *-ize* = to make

synchronize = **Possible Answer** to make things happen at the same time

10. Greek root *aero* = air

the suffix *-ate* = to make

aerate = **Possible Answer** cause something to have air in it

Name _____ Date _____

Selection Vocabulary

 Focus

layer (lā' • ər) *n.* one thickness of something (page 154)

raging (rā' • jing) *adj.* very active and unpredictable (page 155)

survey (sûr' • vā) *n.* an inspection or investigation (page 155)

opposing (ə • pōz' • ing) *adj.* opposite; completely different (page 156)

prediction (pri • dik' • shən) *n.* the act of telling something before it happens (page 156)

severe (sə • vir') *adj.* very serious; dangerous (page 157)

stovepipe (stōv' • pīp') *n.* a thin pipe connected to a stove that directs smoke or fumes out of an area (page 160)

spiraling (spī' • rəl • ing) *v.* moving in the shape of a spiral (page 160)

inspiration (in' • spə • rā' • shən) *n.* the stirring of the mind, feelings, or imagination, especially so that some good idea comes (page 160)

alert (ə • lûrt') *adj.* awake and prepared to act (page 161)

Practice Write the vocabulary word next to the group of words that have a similar meaning.

1. encouragement; stirring; prompting ___inspiration___

2. differing; conflicting; contradictory ___opposing___

3. serious; critical; risky ___severe___

4. aware; watchful; attentive ___alert___

5. wild; unpredictable; turbulent ___raging___

6. forecast; projection; speculation ___prediction___

7. piece; slab; level; ___layer___

8. winding; twisting; turning _____ spiraling _____

9. investigation; study; research _____ survey _____

10. chimney; smokestack _____ stovepipe _____

Apply Draw a line to match each word on the left to its definition on the right.

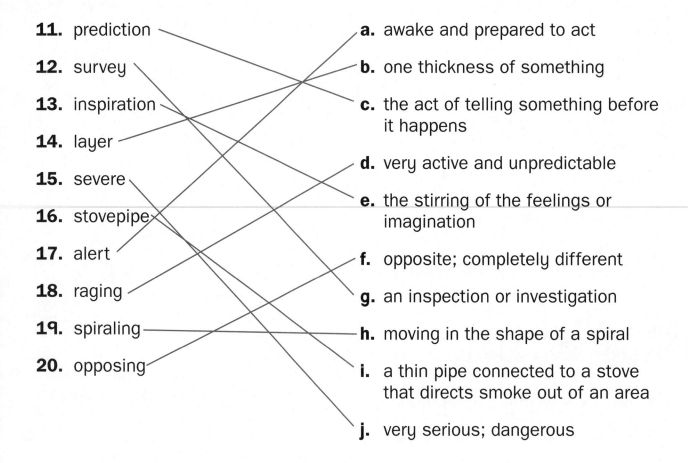

11. prediction

12. survey

13. inspiration

14. layer

15. severe

16. stovepipe

17. alert

18. raging

19. spiraling

20. opposing

a. awake and prepared to act

b. one thickness of something

c. the act of telling something before it happens

d. very active and unpredictable

e. the stirring of the feelings or imagination

f. opposite; completely different

g. an inspection or investigation

h. moving in the shape of a spiral

i. a thin pipe connected to a stove that directs smoke out of an area

j. very serious; dangerous

Name _____ **Date** _____

Formulating Questions and Problems

A good question or problem to investigate:
Possible Answer How does my behavior affect Earth?

_____

_____

_____

Why this is an interesting question or problem:
Possible Answer It is a direct connection between me and a topic of concern. It gives me the opportunity to see how I affect Earth.

_____

Some other things I wonder about this question or problem:
Possible Answer Does my behavior have a direct impact on the environment of my community? Does the behavior of my community have a direct impact on the environment of Earth?

Formulating Questions and Problems (continued)

My investigation group's question or problem:

Possible Answer In what way can we change our behavior to improve our effect on the environment? Will these be passive changes, such as changing basic behaviors, or more active changes, such as forming a litter clean-up group?

What our investigation will contribute to the rest of the class:

Possible Answer We can provide ideas for others on how to improve their behavior. We can help others consider ideas that they might not have discovered.

Some other things I wonder about this question or problem:

Possible Answer Can we change the general attitude of our community? Are there ways we can bring about change in others by changing our behavior?

Name _____   Date _____

Gardener's Almanac

 **Audience: Who** will read your article?
Possible Answer my teacher and other students

Purpose: What is your reason for writing a gardening article?
Possible Answer I want to share my knowledge

about growing lima beans.

Prewriting When you use someone else's knowledge or ideas, you must give that person credit. Find some information about lima beans in each type of source listed below. Write the information you find in your Learning Log, and then use the lines below to begin writing a bibliography. Be sure to use the correct format for each type of source.

Book: **Possible Answer** Greene, Robert. Beans, Beans, and More Beans. Chicago:Showalter Publishing, 2005.

Encyclopedia: **Possible Answer** "The Life of a Lima Bean." Encyclopedia of Crops and Agriculture. 2002 ed.

Internet site: **Possible Answer** "Growing a Better Bean." The World's Most Nutritious Foods. November 29, 2006. The Farmer's Alliance for Healthy Nutrition. January 7, 2007. <http://www. farmersalliance.org/nutritiousfoods/limabeans.html>

Revising
Use this checklist to revise the report of your experiment.

☐ Is your hypothesis clearly stated?

☐ Do your observations and research support the advice you provide?

☐ Have you included enough information from your Learning Log notes and clearly organized them?

☐ Have you cited all your sources in a bibliography?

Editing/Proofreading
Use this checklist to correct mistakes.

☐ Have you used the proper format for each type of source in your bibliography?

☐ Did you check all capitalization, punctuation, and spelling?

☐ Have you read your report more than once to check for correctly used conjunctions throughout your almanac?

☐ Did you review any suspicious information and double-check your facts?

Publishing
Use this checklist to publish your results.

☐ Rewrite your report neatly, or type it on a computer.

☐ Add graphs, charts, or other helpful illustrations to your report.

☐ Share your report with your teacher or a classmate.

Name _____ Date _____

Spelling

Focus

- The prefix *ir-* means "not".
- The prefix *dis-* has several meanings: "opposite" or "lack of" or "not."

- **Root words** were formed from words of other languages, such as Greek and Latin. Here are some roots in the spelling words and their meanings:

port = carry; *sign* = mark

Word List

1. discouraged
2. irregular
3. portable
4. import
5. displace
6. irrelevant
7. sign
8. signify
9. disembark
10. signal
11. exporting
12. national
13. irrefutable
14. porter
15. transportation
16. disinterest
17. signature
18. insignia
19. irrational
20. irreparable

Practice Write the spelling word which is formed by adding the prefix *ir-* or *dis-* to each of the word parts.

1. ir + reparable = __irreparable__
2. ir + refutable = __irrefutable__
3. dis + appearing = __disappearing__
4. dis + interest = __disinterest__

Fill in the root word and write the resulting spelling word on the line.

sign

5. __sign__ ature   signature
6. __sign__   sign

port

7. __port__ able   portable

stella

8. __stella__ r   stellar

Apply Fill in the blanks with the appropriate letters to create a spelling word from the list and write it on the line.

9. p__ort__able = portable

10. __ir__regular = irregular

11. __dis__embark = disembark

12. s__ign__al = signal

13. __ir__relevant = irrelevant

14. in__sign__ia = insignia

15. __dis__appearing = disappearing

16. p__ort__er = porter

17. trans__port__ation = transportation

18. s__ig__n = sign

19. ex__port__ing = exporting

20. im__port__ = import

21. __dis__couraged = discouraged

22. __ir__refutable = irrefutable

23. __sign__ature = signature

24. __ir__reparable = irreparable

25. __sign__ify = signify

26. __dis__place = displace

27. __dis__interest = disinterest

28. __ir__rational = irrational

Name _____ Date _____

Electronic Technology: Retrieving and Reviewing Information

Focus

- Searching for and retrieving information is much easier because of **electronic technology.** The Internet, online encyclopedias, and electronic library catalogs provide quick access to large amounts of information. Knowing how to choose **keywords** for your searches is an important skill in using electronic technology.

- Electronic technology also helps you review the things you have written. **Word-processing programs** can check for errors in spelling and grammar. They will not catch every error, however; you must still proofread your work. For example, homophones and homographs are often overlooked by word-processing programs.

Practice **A word-processing program corrected most of the errors in the paragraph below. However, there are four errors it did not catch. Read the paragraph carefully, and circle the errors.**

Thomas Edison was (borne) in 1847 in Milan, Ohio. During his teen years, Edison worked several odd jobs before becoming a telegraph operator. His (fist) inventions used telegraph technology to send information like stock numbers and vote tallies. Edison became a household name with his invention (off) the phonograph in 1877. People were amazed to (here) voices coming from a machine.

Explain why the word-processing program may have missed these errors.

Possible Answers *Borne* and *here* are homophones. The other words are words that resemble the intended words.

Apply Read the research topics below. Write at least two keywords you would use to begin a search for information about each topic.

1. How do birds know when to migrate?

Possible Answers birds, migration

2. What are the words in Abraham Lincoln's Gettysburg Address?

Possible Answers Lincoln, Gettysburg, Civil War

3. How does milk get from a cow to your refrigerator?

Possible Answers milk, dairy, farm, transportation

4. Where is the tallest tree in the world located?

Possible Answers tallest, tree

5. Who wrote *The Decline and Fall of the Roman Empire?*

Possible Answers author, Roman, Empire, Decline

6. Who is the current president of Angola?

Possible Answers Angola, president

7. Which ocean is the largest?

Possible Answers ocean, largest

8. What is the function of your kidneys?

Possible Answers kidneys, function

Name _____ Date _____

Inflectional Ending -ed

Focus

- Adding the **inflectional ending -ed** to a verb creates the past tense of the verb.

  They **work** from dawn to dusk.
  They **worked** from dawn to dusk.

- Verbs that end with the inflectional ending -ed can also form the past participle. This verb form can be used as a verb or an adjective.

  That **baked** apple smells great!

Practice **Rewrite the following sentences so that they are in the past tense.**

1. The astronauts land their spaceship on another planet.

   The astronauts landed their spaceship on another planet.

2. My friends and I dine in the cafeteria.

   My friends and I dined in the cafeteria.

3. The horses carry the riders along the trail.

   The horses carried the riders along the trail.

4. The workers rip long strips of wallpaper off the wall.

   The workers ripped long strips of wallpaper off the wall.

5. I type my research paper on the computer.

   I typed my research paper on the computer.

6. My calves itch where they touched poison ivy.

   My calves itched where they touched poison ivy.

Apply

A word ending in *-ed* has been boldfaced in each sentence below. On the line, write *V* if the word is used as a verb, or *A* if it is an adjective.

7. **V** A motorcycle **zipped** past us on the freeway.

8. **A** For dessert, Ms. Christo usually eats **canned** peaches sprinkled with sugar.

9. **A** Amy's **knotted** hair took half an hour to untangle.

10. **V** I **switched** places with Jasmine in social studies.

11. **A** I looked closely at the **graded** tests.

12. **A** Luiz and his uncle drank **iced** tea on the porch.

13. **V** The nurse **checked** on the patients in his care.

14. **V** We **shredded** cheese to spread on the pizza.

Word Structure • *Skills Practice 1*

Name _____ Date _____

Selection Vocabulary

Focus

electromagnets (i • lek' • trō • mag' • nits) *n.* plural of **electromagnet:** a piece of iron with wire wound around it. It becomes a magnet when an electric current is passed through the wire. (page 170)

squinted (skwint' • əd) *v.* past tense of **squint:** to partially close the eyes (page 173)

observe (əb • zûrv') *v.* to make a careful study of (page 174)

crane (krān) *n.* a large machine with a long arm that can be moved up and down and in a circle. Cables at the end of the crane's arm are used to lift and move heavy objects. (page 174)

hypothesis (hī • poth' • i • sis) *n.* something that is suggested as being true for the purposes of further investigation (page 175)

positive (po' • zi • tiv) *adj.* having one of two opposite kinds of electric charge (page 179)

negative (neg' • ə • tiv) *adj.* having one of two opposite kinds of electric charge (page 179)

practically (prak' • tik • lē) *adv.* nearly; almost (page 181)

conclusions (kən • klōō' • zhəns) *n.* plural of **conclusion:** something decided after thinking and experimenting (page 181)

Practice Write the vocabulary word on the line that best completes each sentence.

1. The scientist's experiments proved that his ___hypothesis___ was correct.

2. Electricity contains both ___negative___ and positive charges.

3. ___Observe___ closely how the magician makes the cards disappear.

4. The giant crane uses ___electromagnets___ to lift heavy objects.

5. The giant crane uses _electromagnets_ to lift heavy objects.

6. A negative charge is attracted to a _positive_ charge.

7. The builders used a _crane_ to lift steel beams onto the roof.

8. After leaving the dark theater, I _squinted_ because of the bright sunlight.

9. Dr. Wong and Dr. Shepherd drew different _conclusions_ from the X-rays.

10. We had _practically_ finished building the model when my dog sat on it.

Apply Write *C* in the blank if the selection vocabulary word has been defined correctly. Write *I* in the blank if it has been defined incorrectly, and write the correct word on the line.

11. *Positive* means "something that is suggested as being true for the purposes of an investigation."

    ___I___ _hypothesis_

12. To *observe* means "to make a careful study of."

    ___C___ _____

13. *Conclusions* are things decided after thinking and experimenting.

    ___C___ _____

14. *Cranes* are pieces of iron wrapped in wire with electric currents running through them.

    ___I___ _electromagnets_

Name _____ **Date** _____

Making Conjectures

Our question or problem:
Possible Answer Why is it important to
conserve energy?

_____

_____

_____

_____

Conjecture (my first theory or explanation):
Possible Answer I think it is important
to conserve energy because some
forms of energy are not renewable.

_____

_____

_____

As you collect information, your conjecture will change. Return
to this page to record your new theories or explanations about
your question or problem.

Establishing Investigation Needs

My group's question or problem:

Possible Answer Why is it important to conserve energy?

_____

_____

_____

Knowledge Needs—Information I need to find or figure out in order to investigate the question or problem:

A. **Possible Answer** Why is it important to conserve energy? ____

B. _____

C. _____

D. _____

E. _____

Source	Useful?	How?
Encyclopedias		
Books	yes	about energy use and history
Magazines	yes	articles about energy conservation
Newspapers		
Video and Audio Clips	yes	programs on energy conservation
Television		
Interviews, observations		
Museums		
Other	yes	to collect information on solar and wind power

Inquiry • *Skills Practice 1*

Name _____ Date _____

Book Review

Think

Audience: Who will read your book review?

Possible Answer someone interested in this book

Purpose: What do you want your book review to do?

Possible Answer I want to convince other people to read this story.

Prewriting

A book review should summarize the plot, describe the characters, and offer an opinion about the book. Use this graphic organizer to help plan your book review.

Title	**Possible Answer** *Roll of Thunder, Hear My Cry* by Mildred D. Taylor
Author's Purpose	**Possible Answer** to entertain
Summary	**Possible Answer** The Logans are an African American family living in the South in the 1930s. Cassie Logan, the main character, is nine. She learns about racism and its effects. She also finds out why her family's land is so important.
Your Opinions	**Possible Answer** I thought this was an interesting book. The characters were very realistic, and I felt like I knew them by the end. The book deals with tough issues but leaves you feeling hopeful.
Your Recommendation	**Possible Answer** I recommend this book to anyone who likes an exciting plot and strong characters.

Revising Use this checklist to revise your book review.

☐ Did you include an introduction that gives the basic facts about your book, such as title and author?

☐ Have you described the major characters or people who appear in the book?

☐ Does your summary give the reader a clear idea of the plot?

☐ Have you clearly stated your recommendations and opinions about the book?

Editing/Proofreading Use this checklist to correct mistakes.

☐ Did you spell the title and author's name correctly?

☐ Do your nouns and pronouns agree?

☐ Did you check for spelling errors, including those errors missed by a spell-checker?

Publishing Use this checklist to prepare for publication.

☐ Rewrite your book review neatly, or type it on a computer.

☐ Share your book review with the class by reading it aloud.

Name _____ Date _____

Spelling

- When you add the **inflectional ending** **-ed** to a verb, it forms the past tense of that verb. Drop the e if a word ends in e. If a word is more than one syllable and ends in *-er,* do not change the spelling of the base word if the last syllable is not accented. If the word ends in a short vowel followed by a single consonant, then double the consonant.

- The prefix **il-** means "not," and is added to words that begin with *l*.

- **Synonyms** are words with the same, or nearly the same, meaning. A word may have many synonyms that have slightly different meanings.

Word List

1. pictured
2. illiterate
3. laminated
4. registered
5. supposed
6. featured
7. uproar
8. tumult
9. extraordinary
10. pandemonium
11. illegible
12. illegal
13. selected
14. wonderful
15. inflamed
16. illogical
17. marvelous
18. consistent
19. hindered
20. complimented

Practice Add the prefix *il-* or the inflectional ending *-ed* to the following base words to form spelling words from the list. Write the words on the lines.

1. picture   pictured
2. suppose   supposed
3. logical   illogical
4. legal   illegal
5. literate   illiterate
6. laminate   laminated
7. legible   illegible
8. feature   featured
9. register   registered

Spelling (cont.)

10. select   <u>selected</u>

11. inflame   <u>inflamed</u>

12. hinder   <u>hindered</u>

13. compliment   <u>complimented</u>

On the lines, write the spelling words from the list that are synonyms for the following words.

disorder

14. <u>uproar</u>

15. <u>tumult</u>

16. <u>pandemonium</u>

fantastic

17. <u>extraordinary</u>

18. <u>wonderful</u>

19. <u>marvelous</u>

reliable

20. <u>consistent</u>

Apply

On the line, write the spelling word from the list that is related by a common base or root word to each of the following words.

21. hinder   <u>hindered</u>

22. legal   <u>illegal</u>

23. picture   <u>pictured</u>

24. select   <u>selected</u>

25. inflame   <u>inflamed</u>

26. feature   <u>featured</u>

27. laminate   <u>laminated</u>

28. logical   <u>illogical</u>

29. compliment   <u>complimented</u>

30. legible   <u>illegible</u>

31. register   <u>registered</u>

32. literate   <u>illiterate</u>

33. suppose   <u>supposed</u>

34. roaring   <u>uproar</u>

35. consist   <u>consistent</u>

36. wondering   <u>wonderful</u>

37. tumultuous   <u>tumult</u>

38. ordinary   <u>extraordinary</u>

39. pandemic   <u>pandemonium</u>

40. marvel   <u>marvelous</u>

Name _____ Date _____

Pronouns

- A **subject pronoun** replaces one or more nouns in the subject. *I, you, he, she, it, we,* and *they* are subject pronouns.

- An **object pronoun** replaces one or more nouns in the predicate. *Me, you, her, him, it, us,* and *them* are object pronouns.

- A **possessive pronoun** shows ownership. *My, your, her, his, our, your, its,* and *their* are used with nouns. *Mine, yours, hers, his, its, ours, yours,* and *theirs* are used alone.

- **They** organized a yard sale. **She** ran to first base.

- Ishiko came with **me** to the concert. Uncle Tito played with **them.** I gave **her** my notes.

- **Your** sister scored a goal. Therese can have **mine.** This last slice of pie is **yours.**

Practice Circle the pronouns in this paragraph.

On (our) way home from school, Aaron and (I) almost always stop at the little store about a block from (my) house. (He) buys a bottle of soda and nearly finishes (it) before (we) even get back outside. (I) do not like pop. (Its) flavor is too sugary for (me). (I) usually get a couple of apples, but (I) eat (them) slowly. (I) like knowing that (they) are a healthful snack.

Apply The sentences below contain misused pronouns. Rewrite each sentence so that it is correct.

1. Mine brother is studying for him college entrance exams.

My brother is studying for his college entrance exams.

2. They's shirts got splattered with mud from we's driveway.

Their shirts got splattered with mud from our driveway.

3. Us are joining you's class for a field trip to the museum.

We are joining your class for a field trip to the museum.

4. Me have decided to invite thems to mine's favorite restaurant.

I have decided to invite them to my favorite restaurant.

5. It high walls helped protect we from our's enemies.

Its high walls helped protect us from our enemies.

6. Nina's dad drove she and me to our's dance lessons.

Nina's dad drove her and me to our dance lessons.

Grammar, Usage, and Mechanics • *Skills Practice 1*

Name _____ Date _____

Comparatives, Superlatives, and the Prefix *re-*

Focus

- A **comparative adjective** or **adverb** compares one person, action, or thing to another.

- A **superlative adjective** or **adverb** compares one person, action, or thing to several others.

- When forming the **comparative,** most longer modifiers must be preceded by the word **more.**

- When forming the **superlative,** most longer modifiers must be preceded by the word **most.**

- I am **taller** now than I was two years ago.

- That is the **prettiest** painting in the museum.

- Tom was **more patient** than Jim.

- Of all the members of her track team, Kyra runs **most quickly.**

- The prefix *re-* means "again." For example, *reuse* means "to use again."

Practice

Rewrite each sentence below so that it contains a word using the prefix *re-* and a comparative or superlative adjective or adverb.

Possible Answers

Example Emile had to wash the glasses again in the small sink.
Emile had to rewash the glasses in the smallest sink she had ever seen.

1. Suddenly, the rabbit appeared again in the lovely meadow.

   Suddenly, the rabbit reappeared in the loveliest meadow in the park.

2. The good ice cream shop will not open again until next summer.

   The best ice cream shop will not reopen until next summer.

3. I had to listen to LaTonya tell the pleasant story again.

I had to listen to LaTonya retell the most pleasant story I had heard.

4. Julio discovered again a large science kit in his closet.

Julio rediscovered the largest science kit in his closet.

5. Please state your answer again.

Please restate your answer louder than before.

Apply Write the comparative and superlative forms for each word.

6. simple _simpler, simplest_

7. crowded _more or less crowded, most or least crowded_

8. straight _straighter, straightest_

9. likely _more or less likely, most or least likely_

10. early _earlier, earliest_

11. smooth _smoother, smoothest_

12. funny _funnier, funniest_

13. powerfully _more or less powerfully, most or least powerfully_

14. dangerously _more or less dangerously, most or least dangerously_

15. difficult _more or less difficult, most or least difficult_

Name _____ Date _____

Selection Vocabulary

Focus

flickering (flic' • kər • ing) *adj.* burning or shining in an irregular way (page 190)

expands (ik • spandz') *v.* becomes larger (page 191)

propel (prə • pel') *v.* to cause to move forward (page 191)

gusty (gus' • tē) *adj.* blowing in strong, sudden bursts (page192)

reliable (ri • lī' • ə • bəl) *adj.* able to be depended on (page 192)

revolving doors (ri • vôl' • ving dors) *n.* plural of **revolving door:** a door at the front of the building that moves in a circle around a central point (page 193)

converts (kən • vûrts') *v.* changes into something different (page 194)

currents (kûr' • ənts) *n.* plural of **current:** a flow of electricity (page 194)

fossil fuels (fôs' • əl fyoo' • əls) *n.* plural of **fossil fuel:** a fuel formed from the remains of plants and animals. Coal and petroleum are fossil fuels. (page 195)

economical (ek' • ə • nôm' • i • kəl) *adj.* a good use of resources; not wasteful (page 195)

Practice **Circle the word in parentheses that best fits each sentence.**

1. A solar panel (converts, currents) sunlight into electricity.

2. Please use the (fossil fuels, revolving doors) to enter the building.

3. The suitcase (converts, expands) to hold more clothing.

4. Using coupons and watching for sales are (economical, gusty) ways to shop.

5. Burning (currents, ~~fossil fuels~~) is probably not the best way to create energy.

6. This digital watch is much more (~~reliable,~~ flickering) than my old one.

7. Electrical (revolving doors, ~~currents~~) will not flow through insulating materials.

8. Kicking your legs will help (converts, ~~propel~~) you through the water.

9. I knew the batteries were almost dead when the flashlight began (expands, ~~flickering~~).

10. A (reliable, ~~gusty~~) breeze threatened to capsize the sailboat.

Apply   **Write the selection vocabulary word that best answers each question below.**

11. Which word describes someone who always shows up on time and never goes back on his or her word? __reliable__

12. Which word describes what a balloon filling with air does? __expands__

13. Which word describes water moving in the ocean or electricity moving through a wire? __currents__

14. A banker changes French francs into American dollars. Which word describes what he does? __converts__

15. A drooping flag suddenly lifts in a strong breeze. Just as quickly, it droops back down. What kind of wind is blowing? __gusty__

Name _____ **Date** _____

Cause and Effect

When one event causes another to happen, the events have a **cause-and-effect relationship.**

- A **cause** is the reason that an event happens.

- An **effect** is the result of a cause.

- Writers use words such as *because, since, therefore,* and *so* to show the reader that a cause-and-effect relationship has taken place.

Practice   **On a separate piece of paper, answer the following questions about causes and effects in the story "The Wind at Work."**

1. What caused the Dutch to build windmills throughout the flatlands?
   Possible Answer The land was often flooded by the sea.

2. How did harnessing the wind for power affect working conditions? **Possible Answer** People and animals did not have to work nearly as hard.

3. What caused windmills to become less widely used?
   Possible Answer Steam power and gas engines were invented.

4. What effect would using more wind power have on the environment?
   Possible Answer There would be less pollution.

5. What caused humans to begin relying so heavily on fossil fuels?
   Possible Answer Fossil fuels were more reliable.

Apply One-half of each cause-and-effect relationship is missing in the sentences below. Complete the sentences by providing the missing half.

6. When my alarm rang this morning, **Possible Answer** I hopped out of bed and jumped in the shower.

7. Highway 56 is closed; therefore, **Possible Answer** traffic will need to take a detour.

8. Since Annika is bringing a dessert to the party, **Possible Answer** I should bring something to drink.

9. Tucker raised his hand because **Possible Answer** he knew the answer.

10. People are not allowed to skateboard there, so **Possible Answer** I usually go to McReynolds Skate Park.

11. The entire class began laughing when **Possible Answer** the teacher told a joke.

12. Because my grandparents are visiting this weekend, **Possible Answer** we are cleaning the apartment.

Name _____ Date _____

Persuasive Letter

Think

Audience: Who will read your persuasive letter?
Possible Answer the principal

Purpose: What is your reason for writing a persuasive letter?
Possible Answer I want to start a recycling program at our school.

Prewriting

Persuasive writing is used to convince someone to agree with your opinion. Use the graphic organizer below to plan your persuasive letter.

1. Write your viewpoint (main idea).	**Possible Answer** Our school should have a recycling program.
2. Provide facts, examples, and/or expert opinions that support the viewpoint presented.	**Possible Answer** Right now, all of our school's waste goes to a landfill where it will stay forever. At least half that waste is paper, glass, or metals that can be recycled. Harris Recycling will come get our recyclable waste for less than the garbage company charges. As an incentive, we can give prizes to the classrooms or grades that recycle the biggest percentage of their waste.
3. In addition to providing hard facts, use an emotional appeal that you believe will be effective with the audience.	**Possible Answer** We cannot waste precious resources, or there will not be any left when we become adults.
4. End your letter with a conclusion that restates the viewpoint or solution and asks the reader for action, if appropriate.	**Possible Answer** A recycling program is one of the most efficient ways our school can help the environment.

Revising

Use this checklist to revise your persuasive letter.

- ☐ Did you use formal language in your letter and include information that is appropriate for the audience?
- ☐ Does your letter have clear organization?
- ☐ Did you use persausive techniques, like emotional appeal, to convince your reader?
- ☐ Did you avoid using contractions and slang terms?

Editing/Proofreading

Use this checklist to correct mistakes.

- ☐ Did you follow the correct format for a formal letter?
- ☐ Did you check all capitalization, punctuation, and spelling?
- ☐ Have you correctly used compound sentences?
- ☐ Have you correctly used subjective, objective, and possessive pronouns?

Publishing

Use this checklist to publish your persuasive letter.

- ☐ Write your letter on a clean sheet of paper, or type your letter on a computer and print it.
- ☐ Address your envelope, and prepare your letter for sending.

Name _____ Date _____

Spelling

Focus

• Understanding and identifying **Greek roots** and their meanings can help you define and spell difficult and unfamiliar words. Here are some of the Greek roots in the spelling words and their meanings:

meter = measure; ***chron*** = time; ***therm*** = heat

Word List

1. refurnish
2. meter
3. diameter
4. reorganize
5. reintroduce
6. revisit
7. chronic
8. chronicle
9. reaffirm
10. barometer
11. reinforce
12. thermometer
13. reformulate
14. synchronize
15. repurchase
16. chronology
17. regenerate
18. centimeter
19. chronological
20. reapply

Practice

Write the spelling word that results when the prefix *re-* is added.

1. apply   reapply
2. organize   reorganize
3. furnish   refurnish
4. purchase   repurchase
5. formulate   reformulate
6. introduce   reintroduce
7. affirm   reaffirm
8. inforce   reinforce
9. visit   revisit
10. generate   regenerate

Each of the following examples includes at least one Greek root. On the line, write the spelling word that is represented in each of the examples.

11. chron + ological = chronological
12. syn + chron + ize = synchronize

13. therm + o + meter = <u>thermometer</u>
14. chron + ology = <u>chronology</u>
15. baro + meter = <u>barometer</u>
16. centi + meter = <u>centimeter</u>
17. chron + ic = <u>chronic</u>
18. dia + meter = <u>diameter</u>
19. chron + icle = <u>chronicle</u>

Which Greek root in the spelling list is a word by itself?

20. <u>meter</u>

Apply   **Decide which Greek root, when added, correctly spells the word in each sentence. Write the spelling word on the line.**

21. A <u>therm</u>ometer measures heat.   <u>thermometer</u>
22. My little sister is almost one <u>meter</u> tall.   <u>meter</u>
23. The textbook listed the <u>chron</u>ology of events. <u>chronology</u>
24. She suffers from <u>chron</u>ic pain.   <u>chronic</u>
25. Let's syn<u>chron</u>ize our watches.   <u>synchronize</u>

On the line, write the spelling word that is related by a common base or root word to each of the following words.

26. furnished   <u>refurnish</u>
27. purchasing   <u>repurchase</u>
28. application   <u>reapply</u>
29. formula   <u>reformulate</u>
30. introduction   <u>reintroduce</u>

Name _____ Date _____

Regular and Irregular Plurals

Focus | **Most regular plurals** are formed by just adding -s or -es, but **irregular plurals** do not follow any rules for forming the plural.

- For words that end in a consonant and *y,* change the *y* to *i* and then add -es.

- baby, babies
  fly, flies

- For some words that end in *f* or *fe,* change the *f* or *fe* to *v* and add -es.

- loaf, loaves
  shelf, shelves

- For words that end in a consonant and *o,* add either -s or -es. You must use a dictionary to determine which is correct.

- mango, mangos
  potato, potatoes
  rhino, rhinos

- For some words, the plural form is a different word.

- tooth, teeth
  child, children

- For some words, the singular and plural forms are the same.

- deer, deer
  fish, fish

Practice | For each singular word below, write its plural form on the line.

1. floor **floors**

2. bench **benches**

3. candy **candies**

4. loaf **loaves**

5. deer **deer**

6. journey **journeys**

7. boss **bosses**

8. tooth **teeth**

9. hero **heroes**

10. cliff **cliffs**

UNIT 2 Lesson 4

Apply Complete each sentence below by writing the plural form of the word in parentheses on the line. Use a dictionary to check your answers.

11. My _____friends_____ helped me rake leaves out of the garden. (friend)

12. How many _____fish_____ are in the zoo's aquarium? (fish)

13. Dr. Lynn bought _____tomatoes_____ and cucumbers at the market. (tomato)

14. Anna undid the _____latches_____ on her suitcase. (latch)

15. They will travel through the mountains and _____valleys_____ of Montana. (valley)

16. Several _____mice_____ found a way into the pantry. (mouse)

17. We keep the butter _____knives_____ in that top drawer. (knife)

18. Can you name all the _____countries_____ in Africa? (country)

19. Three _____people_____ waited in line in front of me at the deli. (person)

20. The students' _____faces_____ lit up when they heard the news. (face)

21. One night a week, the Alis enjoy watching _____videos_____ together. (video)

22. This book describes the _____lives_____ of a few famous inventors. (life)

Name _____ Date _____

Words with Latin Roots and the Prefix *non-*

Focus
- Many words in the English language contain **Latin roots.** For example, *portable, import,* and *porter* all contain the Latin root *port,* which means "to carry." Identifying and understanding Latin roots can help you define difficult words.

- The prefix **non-** means "not." When combined with a base or root word it forms an antonym of that word.

Practice Each word below uses the prefix *non-* and contains a root word. On the line, write the word's definition. As a hint, you have been provided the meaning of each root word. Use a dictionary if you need help.

1. The Latin root *form* means "shape"

   nonconform = to not give the same shape

2. The Latin root *aqua* means "water"

   nonaquatic = not taking place in water

3. The Greek root *bio* means "life"

   nonbiological = not of or related to living things

4. The Latin root *sens* means "feel"

   nonsensitive = not easily affected by perception

Apply Each group of words uses the same Latin root. Select the correct meaning of the root word from the box, and write it on the line. Write an original sentence using each word.

ray	cut	different	hold

5. variety; variable; various

Latin root *var* means different

Possible Answer Through various speeches to the crew the captain let everyone know that on this ship he was in charge.

6. radiator; radiation; radio

Latin root *rad* means ray

Possible Answer Radio waves are present in the skies.

7. dissect; intersect; section

Latin root *sect* means cut

Possible Answer Omnivores and carnivores often intersect in a food chain.

8. contain; maintain; detain

Latin root *tain* means hold

Possible Answer The man was unable to maintain the pace of the race.

Name _____ Date _____

Selection Vocabulary

Focus

food chain (fōōd chān) *n.* a group of living things that form a chain in which the first living thing is eaten by the second, the second is eaten by the third, and so on (page 204)

food web (fōōd web) *n.* a group of food chains in an ecosystem that are connected (page 204)

ecosystem (ē' • kō • sis' • təm) *n.* all the living and nonliving things in a certain area (page 204)

absorbs (əb • sorbs) *v.* takes in (page 205)

algae (al' • jē) *n.* simple living things that are composed of one or more cells; most algae are plants that do not have roots or flowers. (page 208)

ridges (ri' • jes) *n.* plural of **ridge:** a raised, narrow strip (page 209)

predators (pre' • də • tərz) *n.* plural of **predator:** an animal that hunts and kills other animals for food (page 211)

scavenger (ska' • vən • jər) *n.* an animal that feeds on dead animals (page 211)

omnivores (om' • nə • vors') *n.* plural of **omnivore:** an animal that eats both animal flesh and plants (page 212)

diet (dī' • it) *n.* the food and drink eaten by an animal (page 212)

Practice If the boldfaced definition given for the underlined word in each sentence is correct, write *T* on the line. If the definition is incorrect, write *F* on the line.

1. The mouse scurried quickly through the field, hoping to avoid <u>predators</u>.

animals that hunt other animals for food _____T_____

2. The pool had not been used in years, so <u>algae</u> covered much of the water's surface.

   a kind of tarp or blanket _____F_____

3. A horse's <u>diet</u> consists mainly of roughage and water.

   food and drink eaten by an animal _____T_____

4. As we came around the bend, we startled a <u>scavenger</u> that had been eating.

   an animal that feeds on dead animals _____T_____

5. Dr. Meredith studied the <u>food chain</u> in Lake Superior.

   the different things an animal will eat _____F_____

6. A kitchen sponge <u>absorbs</u> water, but it also breeds bacteria.

   cleans or wipes _____F_____

7. The desert <u>ecosystem</u> is more diverse than you might imagine.

   all the living and nonliving things in an area _____T_____

8. At times, <u>omnivores</u> become predators.

   animals that eat both flesh and plants _____T_____

9. Gum got embedded between the <u>ridges</u> on the bottom of my shoe.

   raised, narrow strips _____T_____

10. A rain forest's <u>food web</u> contains many thousands of creatures.

    a method animals use to get their food _____F_____

Apply Review the selection vocabulary words for "What Are Food Chains and Webs?". On a separate sheet of paper, write five sentences using at least two vocabulary words from this lesson in each sentence.

Name _____ Date _____

Classify and Categorize

Focus Classifying and categorizing are ways of organizing information. They can help you better understand and remember what you read.

- **Classifying** is identifying the similarities that objects, characters, or events have in common with each other, and then grouping them by their similarities.

- **Categorizing** is the act of organizing the objects, characters, or events into groups, or categories.

Practice Reread pages 210–212 in "What Are Food Chains and Webs?". Animals that eat other animals can be categorized in several different ways. On the lines below, list the seven possible categories the text mentions for animals that eat other animals.

1. carnivores
2. secondary consumers
3. tertiary consumers
4. predators
5. scavengers
6. omnivores
7. opportunistic feeders

Apply Scientific classification is used around the world to classify plants, animals, and other organisms. Every living thing on Earth can be categorized into several groups that range from the very general to the very specific—from kingdoms to species. Classify the animals listed in the box by placing them into their appropriate categories in the chart below.

chimpanzee	turtle	mouse	alligator	fruit fly
ladybug	cobra	horse	praying mantis	

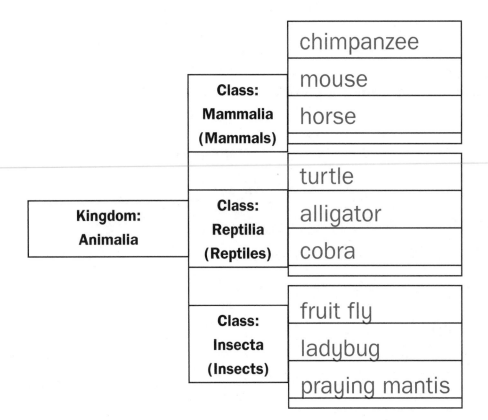

Comprehension Skill • *Skills Practice 1*

Name _____   Date _____

Persuasive Report

Think

Audience: Who will read your persuasive report?
Possible Answer the school board
_____

Purpose: What is your reason for writing a persuasive report?
Possible Answer I want to convince my school
_____
district to use vegetable oil as fuel for its buses.
_____

Prewriting

The graphic organizer below will help you outline your persuasive report. Use the numbered lines to provide supporting facts and details for each subtopic. **Possible Answers**

Topic: Our school buses should run on vegetable oil.

| **Subtopic:** Gasoline is expensive. | **Subtopic:** Gasoline is not clean. |

1. Gasoline prices continue to rise.

2. Gasoline might be running out soon.

1. Fossil fuels cause pollution when they are burned.

2. Our buses use diesel gas, which is even dirtier than regular gasoline.

| **Subtopic:** Used vegetable oil is readily available. | **Subtopic:** We do not need to buy completely new school buses. |

1. Fast food restaurants produce a lot of vegetable oil.

2. Used vegetable oil is free or very inexpensive.

1. The buses' engines need to be modified.

2. The savings would make up for the initial costs.

Conclusion: Our school would set an example by using clean, inexpensive vegetable oil as a fuel.

Revising
Use this checklist to revise the draft of your report.

☐ Is your draft organized according to the outline you prepared?

☐ Are your paragraphs cogent?

☐ Have you included facts and details that support and address your opinion?

☐ Do you have strong opening and concluding paragraphs?

☐ Did you use persuasive techniques to convince your reader?

Editing/Proofreading
Use this checklist to correct mistakes.

☐ Have you correctly capitalized proper nouns?

☐ Have you spelled specialized words correctly and consistently throughout your report?

☐ Did you avoid using contractions and slang terms?

Publishing
Use this checklist to share your draft.

☐ Neatly type your persuasive report and put it in your Writing Portfolio.

☐ Read the draft of your report to a group of classmates.

Name _____ **Date** _____

Spelling

Focus

- Many words feature the prefix **non-**, which usually means "not." It often changes a base word to an antonym.
- Here are some of the **Latin roots** in the spelling words and their meanings:

  sect = cut; **vor** = eat; **carn** = meat; **herb** = "plant"; **jur, jud, jus** = "law"; **omni** = "all"

Practice Remove the prefix *non-* from each word and write the resulting word.

1. nonabrasive   abrasive
2. nonconforming   conforming
3. noncreative   creative
4. nonsense   sense
5. nonstick   stick

Fill in the appropriate Latin root or Latin root form and write the resulting spelling word on the line.

6. __sect__ion   section
7. __jur__isdiction   jurisdiction
8. de__vour__   devour
9. __jur__y   jury
10. carni__vor__e   carnivore

Word List

1. devour
2. nonviolent
3. section
4. nontoxic
5. nonstick
6. jury
7. nonessential
8. carnivore
9. herbivore
10. nonresident
11. dissect
12. intersect
13. noncreative
14. jurist
15. jurisdiction
16. nonsense
17. nonconforming
18. omnivore
19. nonprofit
20. nonabrasive

Apply Write the spelling word that matches each definition on the line.

11. not fierce ___nonviolent___

12. not important ___nonessential___

13. not inventive ___noncreative___

14. not a member of a city ___nonresident___

15. not sticky ___nonstick___

16. not fitting in ___nonconforming___

17. not taking in gains ___nonprofit___

18. not rough ___nonabrasive___

19. not poisonous ___nontoxic___

20. not having meaning ___nonsense___

Determine which Latin root correctly completes the word in each sentence. Write the appropriate Latin root and write the resulting spelling word on the lines below.

21. A _jur_y judges whether a person is guilty or innocent. ___jury___

22. A _carn_ivore eats meat. ___carnivore___

23. The two streets inter_sect_ by the gas station. ___intersect___

24. The _jur_ist did not know if the defendant was guilty. ___jurist___

25. That _sect_ion of the library holds fiction books. ___section___

26. The snake wanted to de_vour_ the mouse. ___devour___

27. A giraffe is a herbi_vore_. ___herbivore___

28. The biologist began to dis_sect_ the frog. ___dissect___

29. I am an _omni_vore. ___omnivore___

30. Which police station has _juris_diction over our neighborhood? ___jurisdiction___

Name _____ Date _____

Possessive Nouns, Possessive Pronouns, and Conjunctions

Focus **Possessive nouns and pronouns** show ownership.

- Add 's to singular nouns and plural nouns that do not end with s to form possessives.

- the pie**'s** flavor
  Chris**'s** textbook
  the children**'s** coats

- Add only an apostrophe to plural nouns that end with s to form possessives.

- students' answers
  cities' laws

- Possessive pronouns do not need apostrophes. They can be used in front of nouns or by themselves.

- **His** bicycle tire needs air.
  Where is **our** new classroom?
  This pencil is **yours.**

- A **conjunction** is a word that connects words or groups of words. A coordinating conjunction joins words or groups of words that are equally important in a sentence: *and, but, or, so, nor, either, yet,* and *for.*

- **Subordinating conjunctions** connect two clauses where one clause is grammatically dependent on the other: *after, although, before, if,* and *when.*

Practice Circle the possessive noun or pronoun that correctly completes each sentence below and underline each conjunction.

1. Some of the trees are already beginning to lose (their, their's) leaves, before anyone predicted.

2. (Omars', Omar's) classmates voted for him to become student treasurer, although Jeremy was better in math.

3. Mrs. Riaz signed all her (employees', employee's) checks on the same day, and she never missed anyone.

4. (My, Mine) favorite actor has a new movie coming out soon, but it is not showing in my town.

5. The (runners's, runners') faces dripped with sweat, and they were exhausted.

Apply Use *and, but,* or *or* to complete each sentence below and circle each possessive noun and underline each possessive pronoun.

6. Next year I will have Ms. Patel for my math __and__ social studies classes.

7. The Suarezes planned to take Nitesh's boat and go sailing, __but__ there was hardly any wind.

8. You need to decide whether we will have pizza, __or__ you will make your famous meatloaf.

9. Dana's soccer team will either score on this kick, __or__ the game will be over.

10. A door slammed somewhere in the house, __and__ then I heard my sister yelling.

11. Tulips, roses, __and__ daisies are Faith's favorite flowers.

12. Mountain climbing is a thrilling activity, __but__ you need professional training before you can use Tim's gear.

13. I want the Hawks to win in the finals, __but__ the Bobcats are expected to win their third title.

14. Dante washed his face, brushed his teeth, __and__ combed his hair before leaving the house.

Name _____ Date _____

Irregular Verbs and the Prefix *mid-*

Focus

The rule for forming the past tense of most verbs is to add *-ed*. **Irregular verbs** do not follow this rule. Instead you must learn the present tense, past tense, and past participle of each verb.

- For example, *run* and *ran* are different by only one letter, but *go* and *went* are completely different words.

- The prefix **mid-** means "at or in the middle of." For example, *midsection* means the section in the middle.

Practice

Use the tense shown at the end of the sentence to decide which irregular verb correctly completes the sentence. Circle the correct choice. Underline the words in the sentences that contain the prefix *mid-*.

1. Most colonists (feel, (felt)) _____ felt _____ strongly about their British rulers. **PAST**

2. In wartime it is often difficult to (found, (find)) _____ find _____ normal, everyday items. **PRESENT**

3. Midway through the final quarter, he (leave, (left)) _____ left _____ the football game to avoid traffic. **PAST**

4. He (come, (came)) _____ came _____ at the midpoint of the conflict to give aid to the Patriots. **PAST**

5. I ((have), had) _____ have _____ never worked past midnight. **PRESENT**

Apply The following paragraphs contain incorrect past-tense verbs. On the line, write the correct past-tense form for each irregular verb.

Last summer my family and I **goed** _____went_____

to Philadelphia. When the trip **beginned** _____began_____

it was raining, but by the time we stopped for lunch, the sun

had **fighted** _____fought_____ its way through the clouds.

At Independence Hall the tour guide **telled**

_____told_____ us the story of the Declaration of

Independence. Afterward I **buyed** _____bought_____ a

postcard from the gift shop. I **writed** _____wrote_____

to my grandmother, telling her about everything we had seen

so far. My dad **thinked** _____thought_____ the postcard

was a thoughtful thing to do.

We **spended** _____spent_____ the next afternoon

watching a baseball game. The best part was when my

dad **catched** _____caught_____ a ball that was hit

into the stands. After we left the stadium, Dad **gived**

_____gave_____ it to my brother.

I **bringed** _____brought_____ my camera on the trip

and **taked** _____took_____ a lot of pictures. Sometime

I will show them to you.

Name _____ Date _____

Selection Vocabulary

Focus

colonies (ko' • lə • nēz) *n.* plural of **colony:** a territory ruled by another country (page 230)

loyal (loi' • əl) *adj.* having or showing strong and lasting support for someone or something (page 231)

settlers (set' • lərz) *n.* plural of **settler:** a person who makes his or her home in a new land or country (page 233)

protest (prō' • test) *n.* to object to (page 234)

liberty (lib' • ər • tē) *n.* freedom from control of another country (page 236)

militia (mə • lish' • ə) *n.* a group of citizens trained to fight and help in emergencies (page 239)

necessities (nə • ses' • i • tēz) *n.* plural of **necessity:** something that is needed (page 243)

pamphlets (pam' • flitz) *n.* plural of **pamphlet:** a small book that has a paper cover (page 244)

published (pub' • lisht) *v.* past tense of **publish:** to print a newspaper, magazine, book, or other material and offer it for sale (page 244)

discharge (dis' • chärj) *n.* dismissal from service or a job (page 248)

Practice Write the selection vocabulary word that best fits each clue below.

1. Dogs are often described with this word.

   Which word is it? _____loyal_____

2. When people do this, sometimes they make signs, gather in large groups, or sign petitions. What is it?

   _____protest_____

3. Many people fought very long and hard for this.

   What is it? _____liberty_____

4. This is a word used when someone is let go from a job.

Which word is it? _____discharge_____

5. The United States was originally made of thirteen of these.

What are they? _____colonies_____

6. This word describes water, clothing, and food.

Which word is it? _____necessities_____

7. These could help you give information to other people.

What are they? _____pamphlets_____

8. This group of people is trained to help others in an emergency.

Which word describes them? _____militia_____

9. These people make their homes in new lands.

They are _____settlers_____.

10. This word describes printed materials for sale to the public.

Which word is it? _____published_____

Apply

On a separate sheet of paper, challenge students to create five sentences using the selection vocabulary words. Each sentence should contain at least two vocabulary words.
Make sure to use each word at least once.

Answers will vary.

Name _____ Date _____

Cause and Effect

When one event causes another to happen, the events have a **cause-and-effect relationship.**

- A cause is the reason that an event happens.
- An effect is the result of the cause.
- Writers use words such as *because, since, therefore,* and *so* to show the reader that a cause-and-effect relationship has taken place.

Review the selection ". . . If You Lived at the Time of the American Revolution" to find out why the following events happened. Write down the cause for each event.

Possible Answers

1. The Patriots dumped England's tea into Boston Harbor because

   they were angry about the taxes on tea
   _____.

2. The British soldiers were called Redcoats because

   their uniforms were red
   _____.

3. Many families were split because

   they had both Loyalist and Patriot family members
   _____.

4. Certain soldiers in the Continental Army were called minutemen because

   they could be ready for battle in a minute
   _____.

5. During the war, paper money lost value because

   too much of it was printed
   _____.

Apply The sentences below are incomplete. Each sentence shows only one half of a cause-and-effect relationship. At the beginning of each sentence, write *C* if you are given the cause. Write *E* if you are given the effect. Then, complete the sentence by adding the missing half.

6. __C__ The front tire of Reggie's bicycle was flat, so

Possible Answer he had to walk to school _____ .

7. __E__ Monika grabbed an umbrella as she left home because

Possible Answer the weather forecast called for rain _____ .

8. __C__ Since our soccer team won nearly all its games,

Possible Answer we will get to play in the finals _____ .

9. __C__ Sophie has books due at the library; therefore

Possible Answer she needs to return them _____ .

10. __E__ A section of our street is closed because

Possible Answer the city is working on the sewer _____ .

Now write your own cause-and-effect sentences using *therefore, since, because,* and *so*.

Possible Answer John missed the bus; therefore he was late for school. _____

Possible Answer Since Jose enjoyed American history, he did his report _____

on the Declaration of Independence. _____

Possible Answer Because it was raining, the baseball game was _____

cancelled. _____

Possible Answer Laura liked basketball, so she tried out for the basketball _____

team. _____

Name _____ **Date** _____

Recording Concept Information

As I read the selection, this is what I added to my understanding of the unit theme Making a New Nation. **Possible Answers**

• ". . . If You Lived at the Time of the American Revolution" by Kay Moore

I learned that Americans made many sacrifices for freedom.

• "The Midnight Ride of Paul Revere" by Henry Wadsworth Longfellow

I learned that the poem is not historically accurate. However, the poem portrays the events in an inspired manner.

• "The Master Spy of Yorktown" by Burke Davis

I learned that African-American spies were key to helping defeat the British and securing America's independence.

• "Shh! We're Writing the Constitution" by Jean Fritz

I learned that the writing of the U.S. Constitution was a long and difficult process and there were several drafts.

• "Give Me Liberty!" by Russell Freedman I learned that the signers of the Declaration of Independence risked their lives by signing the document.

Name _____ Date _____

Knowledge About Making a New Nation

• This is what I know about making a new nation before reading the unit.

Possible Answer America made itself into a new nation when it broke free of England. There were thirteen colonies which later became states. The Revolution was started in part because the colonies thought taxation without representation was unfair.

• These are some things about making a new nation that I would like to talk about and understand better.

Possible Answer What were the battles like during the American Revolution? Could a nation be formed without fighting? What makes our nation unique compared to other nations?

_____

_____

Reminder: I should read this page again when I get to the end of the unit to see how much my ideas about making a new nation have changed.

Name _____ **Date** _____

Ideas About Making a New Nation

Of the ideas discussed in class about making a new nation,
these are the ones I found most interesting.
Possible Answer Many different people
took part in the American Revolution.
The founders played their part, but
many other lesser known individuals put
equal amounts of effort into fulfilling
the goal of independence.

_____

_____

_____

_____

_____

_____

_____

_____

_____

_____

_____

_____

_____

_____

Ideas About Making a New Nation (continued)

Write down the ideas you found most interesting about the selection ". . . If You Lived at the Time of the American Revolution." Discuss your ideas with the class.

Possible Answer Many people made sacrifices during the American Revolution. Because of shortages and the loss of trade many common items were hard to obtain. Everyone who lived in the colonies was affected in one way or another.

Name _____   Date _____

Timed Writing: Persuasive Writing

Think

Audience: Who will read your persuasive writing?
Possible Answer the teacher
_____

Purpose: Why are you writing to persuade?
Possible Answer to convince my teacher that our lunch
_____
break should be longer.
_____

Prewriting   In school, you may be given only a short amount
of time to write an essay or a paragraph. Your
first step should always be to read the directions
carefully. For the assignment below, circle the most important
information in the directions. Then, list three ideas you might
write about to complete the assignment.

   Write a persuasive paragraph about a rule or law that you

think is unfair. Be sure to include at least three sentences

supporting your argument. Also include one sentence that

tells the opposite point of view. You have twenty minutes to

complete the paragraph.

1. **Possible Answers** Kids cannot drive until they are sixteen.
   _____

2. **Possible Answers** Cell phones are not allowed in the classroom.
   _____

3. **Possible Answers** A one-hour limit for using the library's computers.
   _____

_____

Revising Use this checklist to revise your persuasive paragraph.

- ☐ Did you clearly state your opinion in the opening sentence?
- ☐ Did you include three sentences supporting your argument?
- ☐ Did you include one sentence about the opposite point of view?
- ☐ Did you use formal language?

Editing/Proofreading Use this checklist to correct mistakes.

- ☐ Are there any spelling errors?
- ☐ Have you used adjectives to modify nouns and pronouns?
- ☐ Do all the sentences contain correct punctuation?
- ☐ Have you corrected any contractions?

Publishing Use this checklist to prepare your persuasive paragraph for publication.

- ☐ If you have time, rewrite your paragraph neatly on a fresh sheet of paper.
- ☐ Hand in your completed Timed Writing assignment.

Name _____ **Date** _____

Spelling

Focus

• When you add the inflectional ending **-ed** to a verb, it forms the past tense. Drop the e if a word ends in e, and then add the -ed ending. If the word ends in a short vowel followed by a single consonant, then double the consonant.

• **Irregular verbs** are verbs that do not form the past tense by adding -ed: choose, chose; forbid, forbade; creep, crept. Knowing the past tense of irregular verbs will help you prevent spelling mistakes.

• A prefix changes the meaning of the base word it precedes. Identifying prefixes and understanding their meanings can help you figure out the meaning and spelling of a difficult or unfamiliar word. The prefix **mid-** means "the middle." It does not change the spelling of the base word to which it is added.

Word List

1. midnight
2. chose
3. escaped
4. midyear
5. choose
6. downloaded
7. midsection
8. forbid
9. forbade
10. graduated
11. midterm
12. midstream
13. creep
14. crept
15. financed
16. communicated
17. midfield
18. midland
19. employed
20. midsummer

Practice Add the inflectional ending **-ed** to the following base words and write the resulting spelling words on the lines.

1. download _____ downloaded _____

2. employ _____ employed _____

3. communicate _____ communicated _____

4. graduate _____ graduated _____

5. finance _____ financed _____

6. escape _____ escaped _____

Write the present tense and past tense of the irregular verbs in the spelling list. Possible Answers

Present	Past
7. creep	crept
8. choose	chose
9. forbid	forbade

Add the prefix *mid-* to the following base words and write the resulting spelling words on the lines.

10. land __midland__   14. field __midfield__

11. year __midyear__   15. summer __midsummer__

12. night __midnight__   16. section __midsection__

13. stream __midstream__   17. term __midterm__

 **Apply** If the underlined verb in the sentence is incorrect, write the correct form of the verb from the spelling list on the line. If it is correct, write correct.

18. Yesterday, I <u>forbidded</u> him to leave.   forbade

19. We <u>downloadded</u> that new game last week.   downloaded

20. We never <u>communicatted</u> very well.   communicated

21. The couple <u>financed</u> their car payment.   correct

22. The store <u>employed</u> ten people.   correct

23. The sisters <u>creppt</u> downstairs.   crept

24. The mouse <u>escapped</u> from the cat.   escaped

Name _____   Date _____

Comparative and Superlative Adjectives and Adverbs

Focus

Rule	Example
• A **comparative adjective** or **adverb** compares one person, thing, or action to another.	• I am **taller** now than I was two years ago.
• A **superlative adjective** or **adverb** compares one person, thing, or action to several others.	• That is the **prettiest** painting in the museum.
• For most longer modifiers use the word *more* for the comparative, or *most,* for the superlative instead of the *-er* or *-est* endings.	• Tom was **more patient** than Jim. Of all her team members, Kyra runs **most quickly.**

Practice   Write the comparative and superlative forms of each adjective and adverb listed below.

1. quiet quieter, quietest

2. crispy crispier, crispiest

3. hot hotter, hottest

4. soon sooner, soonest

5. excited more or less excited, most or least excited

6. slowly more or less slowly, most or least slowly

7. interesting more or less interesting, most or least interesting

Apply **Cross out the incorrect form of each comparative or superlative adjective or adverb in each sentence. Then, write the correct form on the line that follows.**

8. The three-toed sloth moves the ~~slowliest~~ of all

   land mammals. _____most slowly_____

9. The koala is ~~more fast~~ than the three-toed sloth, but only

   when it is awake. _____faster_____

10. Koalas spend about twenty-two hours a day sleeping,
    making them the ~~more sleepy~~ of all of animals.

    _____sleepiest_____

11. The capybara, a rodent that can weigh more than one
    hundred pounds, is definitely ~~heaviest~~ than an

    average mouse. _____heavier_____

12. The black mamba's speed and deadly bite make it the

    world's ~~dangerest~~ snake. _____most dangerous_____

13. At one hundred fifty years, the reptile that lives ~~most~~
    ~~longly~~ is the Galapagos tortoise.

    _____longest_____

14. The world's ~~largerest~~ spider has a perfect name—the

    Goliath birdeater. _____largest_____

15. With a wingspan of thirteen feet, the Marabou stork has
    the ~~most widest~~ wingspan of all birds.

    _____widest_____

Name _____ Date _____

Homophones and the Suffix *-less*

Homophones are words that sound the same but have different spellings and meanings. The following word pairs are examples of homophones.

there	for	would	so	made	wear
their	four	wood	sew	maid	where

Many words feature the suffix **-less.** This suffix means "without" when added to base or root words.

Hope + less = without hope

Fear + less = without fear

Fill in the blank in each sentence with the appropriate homophone.

rose	rows	threw	through

1. At the end of the school year, I gave a single red

   _____rose_____ to my favorite teacher, Ms. Mendoza.

2. All the _____rows_____ were filled with people awaiting the
   performance.

3. The crowd cheered when the quarterback _____threw_____
   a touchdown in the final seconds of the game.

4. The Millers will have to travel _____through_____ the
   mountains to reach their new home.

Write the word on the line that corresponds with the definition.

| baseless | tireless | careless |
| powerless | seamless | thoughtless |

5. Without seams or interruptions __seamless__

6. Without thought __thoughtless__

7. Without a care __careless__

8. Without getting tired __tireless__

9. Without a base or foundation for a thought __baseless__

10. Identify the two base words that are also homophones. Provide the other half of the homophone pair.

seam, seem

base, bass

Apply **Each underlined word is part of a homophone group. Write another word from the homophone group on the line. Provide a matching homophone and then write a sentence using it correctly.**

Possible Answers

11. Then he said, "Good Night!" and with muffled oar

Silently <u>rowed</u> to the Charleston shore __road or rode__

The road curved around the mountains.

12. A line of black that bends and floats

On the rising <u>tide</u>, like a bridge of boats. __tied__

I tied a ribbon around the gift.

Word Structure • *Skills Practice 1*

Name _____ Date _____

Selection Vocabulary

 **Focus**

aloft (ə • lôft') *adv.* far above the ground (page 259)

muffled (muf • əld) *adj.* made softer or less loud (page 259)

magnified (mag • ni • fīd) *v.* past tense of **magnify:** to make something look bigger than it really is (page 259)

sentinel (sen' • tə • nəl) *n.* a sentry (page 260)

mount (mount) *v.* to get up on a horse (page 261)

gleam (glēm) *n.* a flash or beam of light (page 261)

ledge (lej) *n.* a narrow surface on a cliff or rock wall (page 263)

weathercock (weth • ər • kôk') *n.* a weathervane (page 264)

assigned (ə • sīnd') *v.* past tense of **assign:** to give out as a task (page 269)

spread (spred) *v.* to make or become known by more people (page 269)

Practice Write the word from the word box that matches each definition below.

gleam	mount	muffled	magnified	ledge
assigned	weathercock	aloft	spread	sentinel

1. _____gleam_____ a flash or beam of light

2. _____magnified_____ made something look bigger than it really is

3. _____aloft_____ far above the ground

4. _____spread_____ to make or become known by more people

5. _____ledge_____ a narrow surface on a cliff or rock wall

6. __sentinel__ a sentry

7. __mount__ to get on

8. __assigned__ gave out as a task

9. __weathercock__ a weathervane

10. __muffled__ wrapped or covered to soften the sound or to protect

Apply **Circle the word in parentheses that best fits each sentence.**

11. The sound of the plane was (muffled/assigned), but we still heard it.

12. Michael slowly crawled across the snowy (ledge/weathercock).

13. The balloon was held (aloft/honorable) by the wind.

14. The news will (spread/mount) quickly to the rest of the family.

15. Let's (witness/mount) our horses and ride through the meadow.

16. The (gleam/ledge) of the car blinded me.

Name _____ Date _____

Formulating Questions and Problems

A good question or problem to investigate:

Possible Answer If I lived during the American Revolution which side would I support? What would be my reasons?

_____

_____

_____

Why this is an interesting question or problem:

Possible Answer It gives me an opportunity to investigate the American Revolution in a truly personal way. I could view the Revolution from my own vantage point and make my own decisions, instead of simply taking the side that the text might present.

Some other things I wonder about this question or problem:

Possible Answer Which side would my classmates or my family support? Would their decisions impact my own?

_____

_____

Formulating Questions and Problems (continued)

My investigation group's question or problem:

Possible Answer Which side would we support if we lived during the American Revolution? What are our reasons? What opinions do we share? Where do we have differing opinions?

What our investigation will contribute to the rest of the class:

Possible Answer We will contribute to a class-wide decision on which side to support in the American Revolution. We may also have reasons that will give other groups or individuals ideas to consider.

Some other things I wonder about this question or problem:

Possible Answer Is the decision of my group affected by the opinions of others? Are my decisions affected by the opinions of others? Are these outside opinions beneficial?

Name _____ Date _____

Timed Writing: Expository Writing

Think **Audience: Who** will read your expository writing?
Possible Answer another student

Purpose: What do you want to tell with your expository writing?
Possible Answer why I love to go fishing

Prewriting **Use the Timed Writing Strategies to complete the following assignment. Start by circling the key things you are asked to do in the instructions. Then, list three details you want to include in your expository writing.**

Write a paragraph about your favorite hobby. Be sure to include at least one sentence that describes when you first started doing this activity. Also include two sentences that tell why you enjoy it. You have twenty minutes to complete the assignment.

1. **Possible Answer** I first went fishing with my uncle last year.

2. **Possible Answer** I like being outdoors.

3. **Possible Answer** I like eating the fish I have caught.

Revising

Use this checklist to revise your expository writing.

☐ Did you clearly describe your first time doing the activity?

☐ Did your sentences show the reader why it is your favorite hobby?

☐ Did you use transition words to organize your paragraph?

Editing/Proofreading

Use this checklist to correct mistakes.

☐ Are there any spelling errors?

☐ Do all sentences contain correct punctuation?

☐ Did you correctly use prepositions and prepositional phrases?

Publishing

Use this checklist to prepare your expository writing for publication.

☐ If you have time, rewrite your paragraph neatly on a fresh sheet of paper.

☐ Hand in your completed Timed Writing assignment.

Name _____ **Date** _____

Spelling

Focus

- **Irregular plurals** do not follow the regular rules for forming plurals. They do not end in -s or -es. Sometimes the base word spelling changes to form the plural, and sometimes it does not change at all: *child, children; salmon, salmon; person, people*

- **Compound words** consist of two smaller words that have been combined to form one larger word. These two words keep the same spelling in the compound word.

- Understanding and identifying suffixes and their meanings can help you determine the meaning and spelling of a difficult or unfamiliar word. Many words feature the suffix **-less**. *Less* is a word on its own, but is also a suffix that means "without."

Word List

1. children
2. moonlight
3. noiseless
4. shoemaker
5. salmon
6. wastebasket
7. sleeveless
8. halfway
9. people
10. earsplitting
11. sightless
12. quarterfinal
13. countless
14. tombstone
15. stainless
16. letterhead
17. tireless
18. flyswatter
19. friendless
20. showerhead

Practice The following spelling words are missing one of their base words. Write the missing part of the compound word in the space provided.

1. _____ fly _____ swatter

2. tomb _____ stone _____

3. _____ quarter _____ final

4. _____ half _____ way

5. ear _____ splitting _____

6. letter _____ head _____

7. ___waste___ basket

8. shower ___head___

9. ___shoe___ maker

10. ___moon___ light

On the line, write the spelling word that is formed by adding the suffix -less to each of the following base words.

11. friend ___friendless___

12. stain ___stainless___

13. sleeve ___sleeveless___

14. noise ___noiseless___

15. tire ___tireless___

16. count ___countless___

17. sight ___sightless___

 **Apply** **On the line, write the spelling word that matches each definition.**

18. without sound ___noiseless___

19. without marks or dirt ___stainless___

20. without buddies or pals ___friendless___

21. with a lot of energy ___tireless___

22. too many to count ___countless___

23. without the ability to see ___sightless___

24. without sleeves ___sleeveless___

Name _____ **Date** _____

Prepositions and Prepositional Phrases

Focus A **preposition** shows the relationship between a noun or a pronoun and another word in a sentence.

A **prepositional phrase** is a group of words that begins with a preposition and ends with the object of the preposition.

Example

• We walked **through the blinding snowstorm.**

Practice Circle the prepositional phrases in this paragraph.

Individual Chinese kingdoms began building what would become the Great Wall around the seventh century B.C. The wall was started in the northern part of the kingdom's capital. Other states started building walls for protection during the sixth century. In the third century B.C., the first emperor of China connected the walls into one system. The Great Wall extends 4,160 miles across China's countryside. Many tourists today still visit what remains of the wall.

Apply Write sentences using these prepositions in a prepositional phrase. **Possible Answers**

1. after _We went for ice cream after practice._

2. at _Hank roped a cow at the ranch._

3. from _Our puppy came from an animal shelter._

4. on _On our car's antenna, we have a flag of my dad's old school._

5. under _José skateboarded under a clear blue sky._

6. with _Tamika danced with her father at the wedding._

Improve the paragraph below by adding at least four prepositional phrases to provide more information to the reader. Answers will vary.

                      after school.
Jonah likes to skateboard‸ He often goes with his brother.
                          near the picnic tables
They prefer the lot next to the big oak trees‸ Many kids come
   on the weekend   among the skaters
here to skate‸ There is a lot of competition‸ However, they
                           during the week
also enjoy teaching each other new tricks they learned‸ Their
     beneath the shade of the trees
parents sometimes sit‸and watch them skate.

Name _____ Date _____

Base Word Families, Suffixes *-ment, -able, -ful*

Focus A **base word** can take many different forms when different prefixes, suffixes, and roots are added. When you know the meaning of the base word, you can begin to find the meanings of the words in the base word family.

- The suffix **-ment** means "an action or process, or the result of an action or process." The suffix usually forms nouns as in *government.*

- The suffix **-able** means "capable, having, or worthy of." *Reliable* means "one capable of being relied upon."

- The suffix **-ful** means "full of." *Beautiful* means "full of beauty."

Practice The following words are followed by their base words. Write three more words with the same base word. Use the suffix listed in one of the derivatives. Use a dictionary if you need help.

1. discovered (-able)
Base word: cover

   Possible Answers uncovered, recover, uncoverable

2. agreed (-ment)
Base word: agree

   Possible Answers disagree, agreement, agreeable

3. entrusted (-ful)
Base word: trust

   Possible Answers trusted, trusting, distrustful

4. meaning (-ful)
Base word: mean

   Possible Answers meaningful, meaningless, meant

Apply Now write two sentences for each base word family. Use the base word in the first sentence and one of the derived words in the second sentence. **Possible Answers**

5. cover: Be sure to cover your mouth whenever you cough.

word in the same family: I went to the Lost and Found to recover my hat.

6. agree: My friends and I agree that the school's French fries are too salty.

word in the same family: I made an agreement with my mother to clean my room on Saturday.

7. trust: You should always be able to trust your best friend.

word in the same family: Do not loan money to a distrustful person.

8. defense: There is no defense for rude or unkind words.

word in the same family: The criticism made him defensive.

Name _____ Date _____

Selection Vocabulary

Focus

looting (lōōt' • ing) *v.* stealing valuable things from others (page 280)

commander (kə • man' • dər) *n.* a leader (page 280)

invaders (in • vād' • ərz) *n.* plural of **invader:** a person who breaks into something or some place without being asked or wanted (page 280)

prompt (prompt) *adj.* quick or on time (page 281)

civilians (sə • vil' • yənz) *n.* plural of **civilian:** a person not in the armed forces (page 284)

revealing (ri • vēl' • ing) *v.* making known (page 285)

idle (īd' • l) *adj.* not busy (page 285)

lessen (les' • ən) *v.* to make or become less (page 287)

precautions (pri • kô' • shənz) *n.* plural of **precaution:** something done beforehand to prevent harm or danger (page 287)

portrait (por' • trit) *n.* a likeness of a person that is created by a painter or photographer (page 291)

Practice **Tell whether the boldfaced definition that is given for the underlined word in each sentence below makes sense. Circle *Yes* or *No*.**

1. Our <u>commander</u> let us finish the training early.
   leader .... Yes   No

2. Lily was <u>idle</u> while the rest of us worked hard.
   quick or on time .... Yes   No

3. I hope the doctor can <u>lessen</u> the pain in my back.
   to make or become less .... Yes   No

4. The men were <u>looting</u> the art museum.
   stealing valuable things from others .... Yes   No

5. Lorna is taking <u>precautions</u> against getting a sunburn.
something done beforehand to prevent harm or danger .... Yes No

6. We had <u>prompt</u> service at the new restaurant.
not busy .... Yes No

7. The <u>invaders</u> destroyed every house on the block.
people not in the armed forces... Yes No

8. I painted a <u>portrait</u> of my grandfather.
a likeness of a person created by a painter or photographer...... Yes No

9. The coach is <u>revealing</u> the new quarterback.
hiding .... Yes No

10. <u>Civilians</u> cheered the Confederate Army as they marched through town.
armed forces.. Yes No

Apply   **Circle the correct word that completes each sentence.**

11. John gave a _____ answer to the teacher.
a. prompt   **b.** invaders   **c.** mates

12. The ice should _____ the swelling in your ankle.
a. lessen   **b.** idle   **c.** prompt

13. The thieves are _____ and breaking windows.
a. idle   **b.** looting   **c.** revealing

14. The army asked the _____ to leave the area by midnight.
a. civilians   **b.** genius   **c.** portrait

15. Jordan is _____ the ending to the movie!
a. looting   **b.** mutually   **c.** revealing

Name _____ **Date** _____

Drawing Conclusions

Focus
Writers do not always provide complete descriptions or detailed information about a topic, character, thing, or event, so readers must draw their own conclusions.

- **Drawing Conclusions** requires readers to make statements about topics, events, characters, or things based on information from the text.

Practice
Skim the selection "The Master Spy of Yorktown." Then, next to each person's name below, write a statement (draw a conclusion) about him. Then, record the text clues on which you based your conclusions. **Answers will vary.**

The Marquis de Lafayette: _____

Clues: _____

_____

_____

_____

James Armistead: _____

Clues: _____

_____

_____

_____

Apply   Write about a character, topic, thing, or event. Before you begin writing, identify a specific conclusion about your subject that you want readers to draw. Write a paragraph about your subject below. Then, exchange papers with a partner. When you have finished reading each other's papers, write a conclusion you have drawn and the text clues that support it at the bottom of the page.

Answers will vary.

_____

_____

_____

_____

_____

_____

_____

_____

_____

_____

_____

Conclusion and Text Clues: Answers will vary.

_____

_____

_____

Name _____ **Date** _____

Making Conjectures

Our question or problem:
Possible Answer Can a nation be
formed peacefully?

_____

_____

_____

_____

Conjecture (my first theory or explanation):
Possible Answer I think other nations
formed through peaceful negotiations
and without violence.

_____

_____

_____

_____

As you collect information, your conjecture will change. Return to this
page to record your new theories or explanations about your question
or problem.

Establishing Investigation Needs

My group's question or problem:
Possible Answer Can a nation be
formed peacefully?

_____

_____

_____

Knowledge Needs—Information I need to find or figure out in order to
investigate the question or problem:

A. **Possible Answer** What other nations were formed peacefully?

B. **Possible Answer** How did that nation go about doing it?

C. **Possible Answer** When did they become independent?

D. _____

E. _____

	Source	Useful?	Possible Answers How?
Encyclopedias		yes	to find nations that were formed peacefully
Books		yes	for historical information
Magazines			
Newspapers			
Videotapes, filmstrips, and Audio clips			
Television			
Interviews, observations		yes	for a different perspective
Museums		yes	for historical information
Other:			

Name _____   **Date** _____

Timed Writing: Summarizing

Think

Audience: Who will read your summary?   **Possible Answer**

someone interested in learning about James Armistead

Purpose: What is your reason for writing a summary? **Possible Answer**

I want to share with my readers a few details from James Armistead's life.

Prewriting   Use the Timed Writing Strategies to complete the following assignment. Start by circling the key things you are asked to do in the instructions. Then record three details from the selection that you want to include in your summary.

Reread page 291 of "The Master Spy of Yorktown." Write a short paragraph summarizing the main idea contained on that page. Be sure to include at least three of the most important facts or events. You have twenty minutes to complete this exercise.   **Possible Answers**

1. The Marquis' friendship with James made him join the fight against slavery.

2. The Marquis helped found an anti-slavery group in Paris.

3. The Marquis supported equal rights for the rest of his life.

Revising
Use this checklist to revise your expository writing.

☐ Did you include a topic sentence at the beginning of your paragraph?

☐ Did you include only the most important details?

☐ Did you use your own words? Are any of your sentences too similar to those in the original selection?

Editing/Proofreading
Use this checklist to correct mistakes.

☐ Did you check the spellings of proper names or specialized words against the original selection?

☐ Do all sentences contain correct punctuation?

☐ Are all prefixes, suffixes, and verb endings used correctly?

☐ Have you correctly used prepositions and prepositional phrases?

Publishing
Use this checklist to prepare your expository writing for publication.

☐ If you have time, rewrite your paragraph neatly on a fresh sheet of paper.

☐ Hand in your completed Timed Writing assignment.

Name _____ **Date** _____

Spelling

Focus

- Understanding and identifying suffixes and their meanings can help you determine the meaning and spelling of a difficult or unfamiliar word. The suffix **-able** means "inclined to," or "capable or worthy of."

- The suffix **-ful** means "full of." The suffixes -ful and -able both make the words to which they are added adjectives.

- The suffix **-ment** means "result or process," or "state or quality of," and is added to verbs to form nouns. When a suffix begins with a consonant, the base word usually does not change when the suffix is added, unless it ends with a y.

Word List

1. dependable
2. movement
3. beautiful
4. peaceful
5. experiment
6. reliable
7. reasonable
8. government
9. helpful
10. fearful
11. embankment
12. entertainment
13. agreeable
14. memorable
15. development
16. thoughtful
17. fruitful
18. fashionable
19. encampment
20. marketable

Practice Add the suffixes *-able, -ful,* or *-ment* to the following base words or word parts and write the resulting spelling words on the lines.

1. embank **embankment**
2. reason **reasonable**
3. thought **thoughtful**
4. fear **fearful**
5. help **helpful**
6. fashion **fashionable**
7. beauty **beautiful**

8. experi __experiment__

9. encamp __encampment__

10. market __marketable__

11. fruit __fruitful__

12. entertain __entertainment__

13. agree __agreeable__

14. govern __government__

15. peace __peaceful__

16. develop __development__

17. depend __dependable__

18. move __movement__

19. memory __memorable__

20. rely __reliable__

Apply Match each word to its definition.

21. dependable __H__   **A.** full of beauty

22. movement __D__   **B.** state or quality of being amused

23. beautiful __A__   **C.** able to be sold

24. peaceful __I__   **D.** state or quality of being in motion

25. experiment __J__   **E.** full of fruit

26. reasonable __N__   **F.** full of consideration

27. fearful __G__   **G.** full of fright

28. embankment __L__   **H.** able to have confidence in

29. entertainment __B__   **I.** full of calm

30. thoughtful __F__   **J.** process of testing

31. fruitful __E__   **K.** result of making camp

32. fashionable __M__   **L.** result of building a raised structure

33. encampment __K__   **M.** inclined toward clothing trends

34. marketable __C__   **N.** inclined towards clear thinking

Name _____ Date _____

Electronic Technology: Creating Text

Focus Today, most people write using word-processing programs. Creating a text is faster and easier to do once you have learned how to use **electronic technology.** Many schools and libraries have computers with word-processing programs available to the students.

Practice Write about a classmate's favorite movie or book. First, choose someone to interview. Then listen carefully as he or she describes the plot of the movie or book. Be sure to ask questions to discover why your classmate liked the movie or book. Use the following lines to take notes. Answers will vary.

_____

_____

_____

_____

_____

_____

_____

_____

_____

_____

Apply Now use a word-processing program to write a paragraph about the movie or book. Be sure to tell why it is your classmate's favorite work. When you have finished, print your paragraph and read it to the class. Use the following lines to write an outline for the electronic text you will create. Answers will vary.

_____

_____

_____

_____

_____

_____

_____

_____

_____

_____

_____

_____

_____

_____

_____

Name _____ **Date** _____

Plurals and the Prefix *con-*

Focus

Most **plurals** are formed by adding -s or -es.

- For words that end in a consonant and *y*, change the *y* to *i* and add -es.
- cherry, cherries
  colony, colonies

- For words that end in a vowel and *y*, just add -s.
- key, keys

- For some words that end in *f* or *fe*, change the *f* or *fe* to *v* and add -es.
- wife, wives
  calf, calves

- For most words that end in a consonant and *o*, you add -es.
- potato, potatoes

- For words that end in *o* preceded by a vowel, just add -s.
- radio, radios

- For words that end in *s, z, ch, sh,* or *x*, just add -es.
- scratch, scratches

Many words feature the prefix **con-.** This prefix is from the Latin meaning "with, join, or together."

Connect = to join **with**, or establish communication with

Conspire = to join **with** another person or group sharing a common goal

Practice

Complete the following list by filling in the blanks with the correct singular or plural form of each word. Circle the words that contain the prefix *con-.*

	Singular	Plural		Singular	Plural
1.	month	months	**6.**	idea	ideas
2.	(confederation)	confederations	**7.**	wish	wishes
3.	consequence	(consequences)	**8.**	boss	bosses
4.	fox	foxes	**9.**	conjunction	(conjunctions)
5.	citizen	citizens	**10.**	hero	heroes

Write the word with the prefix *con-* on the line corresponding to its definition.

concede	consequence	contend
constrain	context	confederation

11. Joined with a group of states

   confederation

12. To force with restrictions in a strained or

   difficult manner   constrain

13. The joining of text together so that it can

   show its meaning   context

14. To cede, or yield, with hesitance

   concede

15. To struggle with   contend

16. A conclusion made with logic, or following a

   sequence of events   consequence

Name _____ Date _____

Selection Vocabulary

Focus

character (kâr' • ək • tər) *n.* all the qualities that make a person or thing different from others (page 302)

allegiance (ə • lē' • jəns) *n.* faithful support of a country, person, group, or cause (page 303)

central (sen' • trəl) *adj.* main; chief (page 303)

delegates (de' • li • gəts) *n.* plural of **delegate:** a person who is chosen to act for others (page 303)

concern (kən • sûrn') *n.* something important to a person (page 303)

league (lēg) *n.* a number of people, groups, or countries joined together for a common purpose (page 304)

contribute (kən • trib' • yo͞ot) *v.* to give (page 304)

eavesdroppers (ēvz' • drop' • rz) *n.* plural of **eavesdropper:** a person who listens to other people talk without letting them know he or she is listening (page 308)

accomplishment (ə • kom' • plish • ment) *n.* achievement (page 309)

rumors (ro͞o' • mərz) *n.* plural of **rumor:** a story or statement passed from one person to another as truth with no proof (page 309)

Practice Write the vocabulary word next to the group of words that have a similar meaning.

1. stories; gossip _____rumors_____

2. loyalty; support _____allegiance_____

3. busybodies; listeners _____eavesdroppers_____

4. main; most important; major _____central_____

5. donate; give; volunteer _____contribute_____

6. group; confederation _____league_____

7. achievement; success _accomplishment_

8. important; worry _concern_

9. representative; person chosen _delegates_

10. quality; personality _character_

Apply Match each word on the left to its definition on the right.

11. league

12. eavesdroppers

13. central

14. delegates

15. accomplishment

16. concern

17. character

18. contribute

a. main; chief

b. a number of people, groups, or countries joined together for a common purpose

c. something important to a person

d. to give

e. people who are chosen to act for others

f. people who listen to other people talk without letting them know they are listening

g. all the qualities that make a person or thing different from others

h. achievement

Name _____ Date _____

Research Report

Think

Audience: Who will read your research report?

Possible Answer my classmates

Purpose: What is your reason for writing a research report?

Possible Answer I want to tell people about the Bill of Rights.

Prewriting

Note cards will help you organize the answers you find. On each card, record the details you will need later for your bibliography. Fill in the sample index card below to practice.

Bill of Rights

First Amendment— Freedom of speech, freedom of press, freedom of religion, freedom of peaceable assembly, freedom to petition the government

Second Amendment— right to bear arms

Third Amendment— prevents government from quartering soldiers

Fourth Amendment— unreasonable search and seizure

Possible Answers

Question: What is the first amendment?

Answers: freedom of speech, press, religion, peaceable assembly, right to petition the government

Type of source: book

Author: Krull, Kathleen

Title: *A Kids' Guide to America's Bill of Rights*

Pub. City: New York

Pub. Name: Avon Books

Pub. Date: 1999

Pages: 12

Revising — Use this checklist to revise your note cards.

☐ Did you rewrite the information you found in your own words?

☐ Did you include bibliographic information for each source?

☐ Did you use clear subject headings?

Editing/Proofreading — Use this checklist to correct mistakes.

☐ Did you use quotation marks if you needed to quote an author's exact words?

☐ Did you check the spellings of proper names or specialized words against the original selection?

☐ Did you check proper nouns and quotations to make sure they are capitalized correctly?

Publishing — Use this checklist to see if you are ready to begin writing your report.

☐ Do your note cards contain enough facts, examples, and explanations for you to be able to write an informative research report?

☐ Are your note cards organized so that your report will have a beginning, middle, and end?

Name _____ Date _____

Spelling

Focus

• A prefix changes the meaning of the base word it precedes. Identifying prefixes and understanding their meanings can help you figure out the meaning and spelling of a difficult or unfamiliar word. The prefix **con-** means "with," or "together."

• The inflectional ending **-ing** is used in the participial form of verbs. These words can function as verbs, adjectives, or nouns. If a word ends in e, drop the e before adding the inflectional ending -ing. If a word ends in a y or x, the spelling of the base word stays the same when you add the inflectional ending -ing.

Word List

1. conform
2. conclusions
3. substituting
4. relaxing
5. concurrent
6. engineering
7. condense
8. liquidating
9. reducing
10. constrain
11. confirm
12. discharging
13. memorizing
14. delegating
15. configure
16. devastating
17. concave
18. marrying
19. concede
20. confront

Practice On the line, write the spelling word that results when the prefix con- is added to the following base words or word parts.

1. cede — concede
2. cave — concave
3. form — conform
4. current — concurrent
5. clusions — conclusions
6. strain — constrain
7. firm — confirm
8. front — confront
9. dense — condense
10. figure — configure

On the lines, write the spelling words that drop the final *e* before adding the inflectional ending *-ing.*

11. substituting

12. liquidating

13. reducing

14. discharging

15. memorizing

16. delegating

17. devastating

On the lines, write the spelling words whose base words do not change when adding the inflectional ending *-ing.*

18. relaxing

19. engineering

20. marrying

Apply   On the line, write the spelling word that is related by a common base or root word to each of the following words.

21. inform   conform

22. relaxation relaxing

23. reduction   reducing

24. liquid   liquidating

25. strained   constrain

26. front   confront

27. married   marrying

28. conclude   conclusions

29. confirmation confirm

30. memory   memorizing

31. conceding   concede

32. cave   concave

33. discharge   discharging

34. substitute substituting

35. current   concurrent

36. engineer   engineering

37. devastate   devastating

38. condensation condense

39. delegate   delegating

40. figure   configure

Spelling • *Skills Practice 1*

Name _____ Date _____

Capitalization

Focus

- Quotations are capitalized when they are complete sentences or when they begin sentences.

- Always capitalize proper nouns, even when they are used as adjectives.

- Personal titles are capitalized only when they are part of a name.

- *A, an, the, but, and, to,* and *of* are not capitalized in titles unless they are the first or last word.

- Patrick Henry is remembered for saying, "Give me liberty, or give me death."

- Swiss watch
  Franklin stove

- my grandpa, our president
  Grandpa Miller,
  President Ford

- *In the Heat of the Night*
  Articles of Confederation
  Everything on a Waffle

Practice Circle the words that should begin with a capital letter.

1. the fourth of july celebrates the signing of the declaration of independence.

2. our first president, general george washington, said: "it is better to offer no excuse than a bad one."

3. one of the few movies made about the american revolution is drums along the mohawk.

4. the book come to the cowpens! describes a battle between american and british forces.

5. a painting of benjamin franklin hangs in the national portrait gallery in washington, d.c.

Apply   Draw three lines under each letter that should
have been capitalized. Draw a slash through each
letter that should not have been capitalized.

My brother, Brian, attends Thomas Jefferson high school.

He is on the Soccer Team. Each labor day, a fundraiser is

held to raise money for the Jefferson patriots' sports teams.

Tables filled with donated items line the High School's

hallways. Everything is for sale. The high school's Principal,

Henry Showalter, kicked off the event by announcing, "let the

sale begin!"

While the sale was happening inside, games and other

activities were being held on the High School's front lawn. My

brother's Coach sat in the dunking booth for a while. Brian took

his chance, and his second toss sent coach Harris splashing

into the water. It was the funniest thing I have ever seen!

Name _____ Date _____

Comparatives and Superlatives

Focus

- A **comparative adjective** or **adverb** compares one person, thing, or action to another.

- A **superlative adjective** or **adverb** compares one person, thing, or action to several others.

- When forming the **comparative**, use the word *more* for most longer modifiers, or *most* for the **superlative** instead of the *-er* or *-est* endings.

- I am **taller** now than I was two years ago.

- That is the **prettiest** painting in the museum.

- Tom was **more patient** than Jim. Of all her team members, Kyra runs **most quickly.**

Practice   Write the comparative and superlative forms of each adjective and adverb listed below.

1. late   later, latest
2. low   lower, lowest
3. bright   brighter, brightest
4. fearful   more fearful, most fearful
5. bad   worse, worst
6. good   better, best
7. pretty   prettier, prettiest
8. famous   more famous, most famous

Apply Cross out the incorrect form of each comparative and superlative adjective and adverb in the following paragraph and write the correct form above it.

Animals are the ~~interestingest~~ *most interesting* and sometimes the ~~most strangest~~ *strangest* things on Earth.

Did you know that the Goliath beetle, weighing 3.5 ounces, is the ~~heavier~~ *heaviest* insect in the world? The sailfish, at sixty-eight miles per hour, swims ~~quickliest~~ *most quickly* of all fish. The Australian sea wasp has the ~~more painful~~ *most painful* sting of all animals. The two-toed sloth moves ~~slowest~~ *slower* than any other mammal and spends most of its life in trees. Howler monkeys yell ~~louder~~ *loudest* of all primates. Their voices can be heard up to three miles away.

Name _____ **Date** _____

Selection Vocabulary

utter (ut' • ər) *v.* To express out loud (page 326)

draft (draft) *n.* A rough copy of something written (page 327)

rights (rīts) *n.* Plural of **right**: a just, moral, or lawful claim (page 328)

declarations (dek' • lə • rā' • shəns) *n.* plural of **declaration**: written statement that makes something known (page 328)

bombarded (bom • bärd' • əd) *v.* Past tense of **bombard**: to attack with bombs or heavy fire from big guns (page 329)

retreat (ri • trēt') *v.* To move back (page 329)

debate (di • bāt') *n.* A discussion between groups that do not agree (page 329)

exposing (ik • spōz' • ing) *v.* Leaving open or without protection (page 329)

composition (kom' • pə • zish' • ən) *n.* Something put together or created, especially something written (page 331)

treason (trē' • zən) *n.* The betraying of one's country by helping the enemy (page 333)

Practice Write *T* in the blank if the sentence describing the vocabulary word is true. Write *F* if the sentence is false. For every *F* answer, write the word that fits the definition.

1. A *composition* is a discussion between two groups that do not agree. ___F___ ___debate___

2. *Treason* is betraying one's country by helping the enemy. ___T___ _____

3. To *expose* is to express something out loud. ___F___ ___utter___

4. When something is attacked with bombs and heavy fire from big guns, it is being *bombarded*.

_____T_____ _____

5. To *retreat* is to move back. _____T_____ _____

6. A *declaration* is a rough copy of something written.

_____F_____ draft _____

7. *Compositions* are just, moral, or lawful claims.

_____F_____ rights _____

8. A *declaration* is a written statement that makes something known.

_____T_____ _____

9. Leaving something without protection is *exposing* it.

_____T_____ _____

Apply Review the vocabulary words and definitions from "Give Me Liberty!". Write three sentences using the vocabulary words provided. **Possible Answers**

10. debate I had a debate with my friend about which basketball team was better.

11. composition Jamilla had to write a composition about the book she had just read for her English class.

12. treason Benedict Arnold committed the most famous act of treason in American history.

Main Idea and Details

 **Focus** Authors organize their writing into a **main idea** supported by **details.**

- A main idea should be clear and focused.
- A main idea should have supporting details. Details provide additional information about the main idea.

Practice **Read the paragraph on page 331 that begins "Congress then turned . . ." and answer the following questions.**

Possible Answers

1. What is the main idea of this paragraph?

   Jefferson's original wording of the Declaration of Independence

   was changed by Congressional delegates.

2. Write three details from the paragraph that support the main idea.

   a. Whole paragraphs were taken out, and new words and phrases

   were added.

   b. In all, nearly one hundred changes were made.

   _____

   c. John Adams thought that some of the changes were good but

   that some of Jefferson's best writing was taken out.

Apply Write a paragraph for each of the two topic sentences provided below. Use sentences for each paragraph that support the main idea stated in the topic sentence.

Topic 1. Sentence: Thomas Jefferson's writing of the Declaration of Independence was influenced by what he had already read about individual rights.

Possible Answer Jefferson had read the writings of philosopher John Locke. Locke argued that people were born with certain natural rights. Jefferson had also read Thomas Paine's Common Sense, a popular pamphlet in colonial America. He would have known that Virginia and some other states already had declarations of rights.

Topic 2. Sentence: At first the colonies were not united in their desire to declare independence from Britain.

Possible Answer The first vote had only nine colonies voting for independence. Pennsylvania and South Carolina changed their votes the next day. A short time later, Delaware joined the others. New York never opposed independence, but its delegates took two weeks to decide. Finally, the vote was unanimous.

Name _____ Date _____

Research Report

Audience: Who will read your research report?

Possible Answer my classmates

Purpose: What is your reason for writing a research report?

Possible Answer I want to tell people about the Bill of Rights.

Use this example of a bibliography to cite multimedia sources used during your investigations.

Bibliography

BOOKS: Author (last name first). Title of Book (underlined).

City of Publication: Publisher, Copyright date.

INTERNET: "Post Title" (in quotations). Site Title (underlined).

Post date or last update. Site sponsor. Date accessed.

<electronic address>

Multimedia sources can help with your research. They can also make your report more informative and more interesting to your audience.

Now think of two ways to use multimedia sources to enhance your research report. For each idea, list a place where you could look for that source.

1. What: __**Possible Answer** a copy of the original Bill of Rights__

Where: __**Possible Answer** on the Internet__

2. What: __**Possible Answer** a painting of James Madison__

Where: __**Possible Answer** in a book at the library__

Revising — Use this checklist to revise your multimedia sources.

☐ Do you have materials from multimedia sources in one of the following formats: graphics, audio, or video?

☐ Will the multimedia sources help enhance your paper?

☐ Have you prepared the materials from multimedia sources that you will use?

☐ Are there any additional multimedia sources you could include?

Editing/Proofreading — Use this checklist to correct mistakes.

☐ Do you have the information you need to list your multimedia sources in a bibliography?

☐ Have you clearly labeled each photograph, map, or other illustration so that your audience knows what graphic they are seeing?

Publishing — Use this checklist to prepare your multimedia sources for a research report.

☐ Decide if your multimedia sources will be used in a paper, during a presentation, or both.

☐ Meet with your teacher to discuss which multimedia sources will work best for your classroom.

Name _____ **Date** _____

Spelling

Focus

- A **comparative adjective** or **adverb** compares one person, thing, or action to another. A **superlative adjective** or **adverb** compares one person, thing, or action to several others. Example: *I am **shorter** than my sister. I am the **shortest** in my family.*

Form the comparative by adding *-er* to the base word, or the word *more* to most longer modifiers. Form the superlative by adding *-est* to the base word, or the word *most* to most longer modifiers. Follow the "drop-the-e rule" and "change-the-y-to-i rule" when adding these endings.

- **Synonyms** are words with the same, or nearly the same, meaning. A word may have many synonyms that have slightly different meanings.

Word List

1. opposed
2. against
3. prettier
4. prettiest
5. jubilant
6. exultant
7. younger
8. youngest
9. disaster
10. misfortune
11. greater
12. greatest
13. nourishment
14. sustenance
15. funnier
16. funniest
17. decrease
18. diminish
19. livelier
20. liveliest

Practice Add *-er* or *-est* to the following base words to form the comparative and superlative spelling words.

1. lively + *-er* = __livelier__
2. lively + *-est* = __liveliest__
3. young + *-er* = __younger__
4. young + *-est* = __youngest__
5. pretty + *-er* = __prettier__
6. pretty + *-est* = __prettiest__
7. great + *-er* = __greater__
8. great + *-est* = __greatest__
9. funny + *-er* = __funnier__
10. funny + *-est* = __funniest__

On the lines, write the spelling words that are synonyms for the following words or phrases.

not in favor of

11. opposed

12. against

thrilled

13. jubilant

14. exultant

hardship

15. disaster

16. misfortune

lessen

17. decrease

18. diminish

food

19. nourishment

20. sustenance

Apply **On the line, write the spelling word that correctly completes the sentence. Use the base word in parentheses plus a comparative or superlative ending.**

21. That show is (funny) than the previous one. funnier

22. My father is the (young) of all his brothers. youngest

23. Is the dress over there (pretty) than this one? prettier

24. Is Fluffy (young) than Spot? younger

25. *Dancing Shoes* is a (lively) song than *Sad Sadie*. livelier

26. Was that the (great) movie you have ever seen? greatest

27. Who is the (funny) person you know? funniest

28. That is the (pretty) baby I have ever seen. prettiest

29. Is one trillion (great) than one quadrillion? greater

30. Chirpy is the (lively) of all our birds. liveliest

Name _____ **Date** _____

Electronic Technology: Revising Text

Focus

Today, most people write using word-processing programs. **Revising a text** is faster and easier to do once you have learned how to use electronic technology. Many schools and libraries have computers with word-processing programs available to the students.

Practice

1   2   3   4   5   6   7   8   9

1. You want to remove a paragraph. After you have highlighted it, you click _____6, Cut_____.

2. To place the paragraph in another part of the text, you click _____7, Paste_____.

3. You decide you do not want the paragraph there after all. You click _____8, Undo_____.

4. To save your work, you click _____3, Save_____.

5. To open a file you saved earlier, you first need to click _2, Open existing file_.

6. You have finished revising and editing, but you want to check the spelling of your work. You click _5, Spell-Checker_.

Apply   Type these two sentences on a computer: "Thomas Jefferson did not want to write the Declaration of Independence. He wanted John Adams to write the first draft." Using the toolbars on the computer, scramble the two sentences together. Finally, pass your scrambled sentences to a partner and have him or her unscramble the sentences using the toolbar.

Answers will vary.